OTHER
Harlequin Romances
by MARGARET ROME

THE GIRL
AT DANES' DYKE

by

MARGARET ROME

HARLEQUIN BOOKS   TORONTO
WINNIPEG

Original hard cover edition published in 1975
by Mills & Boon Limited

SBN 373-01939-4

Harlequin edition published January 1976

Printed in Canada

CHAPTER ONE

THE hem of her raincoat was slapping a stinging tattoo against calves numbed by gusting wind and driving rain. Ahead, like a length of casually-flung grey ribbon, stretched an infinity of road across which moorland sheep meandered without fear, their immunity from traffic and pedestrians guaranteed by elements marshalling for one grand slam before the last hour of daylight became swallowed into dusk.

The girl stumbled on, head down, hands clasped tightly around the collar of her coat, oblivious to nature's warning signals, conscious only of overriding fear and an urge to put as much distance as possible between herself and the horror that lay behind her to the west. Mercifully, her mind was blank, otherwise the expanse of bleak, rain-slashed moorland, its only relativity to man showing in a string of gaunt pylons, an occasional shepherd's hut and a scattering of sheep shelters, might have caused her to panic. As it was, she welcomed the absence of human life—people did not necessarily represent humanity, people could be cruel, savage and totally devoid of compassion.

She breasted a rise, then stopped dead, gasping as she caught the full impact of a demoniacal wind. It tore at her dragging feet when she tried to push on, punched unfairly behind her sagging knees, then when her stripling limbs were bent almost double rain turned to a deluge that did not cease until long after the battered figure had slid senseless to the ground...

Pain penetrated her stupor. A cruel grip around her arm preceded a vigorous shaking that continued, unheeding of her gasped protest. A voice thundered: 'What the devil... Who are you?'

'Raine...' she murmured, hoping the small remnant of information might encourage the owner of the voice to leave her alone.

'I'm well aware of the rain!' The voice boomed back, laced with sarcasm. 'Were it not that poor visibility caused me to slow down to a crawl you might well have felt the weight of my car across your body.' Her head snapped back as roughly he hauled her to her feet. 'You're another of those damned hippies, I suppose?'

The accusation ripped through the darkness accompanied by a flash of lightning that for a split second illuminated the figure towering over her. Through rain-tangled lashes she glimpsed massive shoulders shrugged into yellow oilskins, a shock of hair, red as blood, plastered against a brow furrowed into deep channels and a face half obscured by a beard so that attention was directed to eyes glaring so fiercely they seemed to project green sparks.

Her look of naked terror so surprised him he released his grip, and immediately she sagged and would have fallen but for the speed with which he scooped her back into his arms. Desperately, she tried to struggle out of his clutches, sobbing her

6

fear of the intimidating giant built like a Viking and possessing a voice capable of shaking the ground beneath her feet. As if in fear of her life, she beat punitive fists against his chest and screamed hysterically: *'No! No! Please don't, I beg of you ...'* She fought until her small reserve of strength was exhausted, but the grip of the man who held her merely tightened all the more as she railed against his silent domination. Then finally, with a suddenness that caught him off guard, her slightly body crumpled against him and she slid gently into oblivion.

Happily, she was unaware of the muttered curses that accompanied his efforts to heave her into his car, nor did she hear his irritable voice calling for assistance when, after an hour's driving in treacherous conditions, he finally swung the car into a drive and drew up in front of a flight of steps leading up to a house shrouded in mist, its grim outline broken only by one small window throwing a beam of light upon tangled shrubs clinging to rough, grey walls.

'Simeon! Hurry, man, give me a hand out here!' In answer to his call, the door was thrown open and an elderly manservant stood gaping as his master brushed past him carrying a half-drowned creature in his arms. 'Don't just stand there, fetch towels, a hot drink—no, brandy might be better,' he decided, as lamplight fell upon the girl's face, emphasizing an alarming pallor.

'A girl!' The man's jaw fell open. 'You've brought a girl to Danes' Dyke?'

'I did not bring her, she was foisted upon me,

and the sooner you do as I ask the sooner she'll be on her way!'

Bombarded by heavy sarcasm, the old man backed away, scowling, and went to do as he was bid.

Raine coughed. A stream of fiery liquid was burning her throat and her head was caught by a vice-like grip ready to foil any attempt she might make to turn away. 'Drink!' she was ordered, then made to obey. She almost choked when once again the glass was pressed against her lips and spirit poured forcibly down her throat. She spluttered, choked by brandy fumes, then felt suddenly afire as tingling warmth began penetrating her numbed body.

'Enough ... please, no more!' she gasped when the hand holding the glass loomed back into view.

'Perhaps you're right,' the deep masculine voice boomed. 'The objective is to revive, not to intoxicate, though I've been told some of you people have quite a capacity for alcohol.'

Her head was swimming, but she sought out the owner of the voice, bewildered by his projected contempt. 'I don't understand...' When her voice wobbled she took herself to task and her resulting words sounded faintly prim. 'To which people do you refer?'

'Never mind that just now,' he clipped, releasing her head so as to move directly in front of her. 'If you'll tell me where you are staying my man will go along and fetch someone back here to pick you up.'

She slumped against a cushion, fighting the panic his words had aroused.

She could tell him nothing because she could remember nothing!

Frantically, she tried to recall from where she had come and in which direction she had been heading, but it was as if the cold that had penetrated her body had found its way to her brain.

'I can't...' she whispered, clutching hard to whirling senses. 'I can remember nothing ... nothing at all.'

'You must remember something!' he growled. 'Your name—what's your name?'

'Raine...!' she began eagerly, seizing upon the memory like a straw—but her surname remained elusive.

When her distressed glance pleaded for understanding he expelled an exasperated breath. 'The last thing you remembered before passing out was rain, so naturally rain is your first recollection. But what is your *name*?' he stressed. 'It is important that you should try to remember.'

'Master Thor!' A summons came from the direction of the doorway and the man swung round to answer.

'She's not ready yet, Simeon, I must prise out of her sufficient information to give a clue to her destination. Give me five more minutes,' his tone held grim promise, 'by that time I'll have found out all I need to know.'

As he turned back to her his bulk wavered before her eyes. Drowsily, she forced her eyelids apart, but warmth both inside and out was her undoing and gradually twin crescents of lashes began drooping against cheeks flushed to the colour of a rose.

'Your name?' Dimly she heard the hammered question. 'What is your name?'

Her limbs felt fluid as she nestled deeper into the comfortable sofa. 'Name,' she repeated. Then on a small note of wonder: 'Thor—Norse god of thunder!' She struggled to lift heavy lashes, then, with slumbrous eyes fixed on his glowering features, she rambled wildly, 'If you really are Thor, show me your hammer, your belt and your iron gloves ...' before surrendering to the call of utter exhaustion.

The roughness of calico sheets against her cheek was her first intimation of strange surroundings. Warily, she peeped from beneath half-closed lids and was depressed by the gloominess of a room darkened by curtains of heavy chenille. Soaring high above her bed was a ceiling stained brown with damp, and around the walls, like sentinels placed to guard the stranger occupying the giant four-poster, was ranged furniture carved from solid oak, a wardrobe broad enough to accommodate a giant, a chest of drawers, a dressing-table supported a yellowed, fly-blown mirror with a solitary china candlestick reflected upon its surface.

The fear that had become a part of her reared its head when a tap on the door echoed around the room. 'Come in ...!' she quavered, wondering, as she fingered the lace collar nestling against her throat, who had helped her into the surprisingly attractive nightdress. A man entered in response to her call and to her relief she recognized him. 'Good morning! It's Simeon, isn't it? How nice of you to bring me breakfast.'

She flinched when the tray he was carrying made noisy contact with the surface of a bedside table. 'You'll be wanting to go when you've finished this.' The statement, sounding almost like a threat, was accompanied by a suspicious scowl.

Her uncertain smile faded and was replaced by colour that flooded her cheeks a mortified pink. 'Will I...?' she stammered, then when his scowl deepened, 'Yes, of course I will, I mustn't impose upon your hospitality.'

A cackle which she supposed was meant to indicate mirth escaped the old man's lips. 'Hospitality? Necessity, more like! Women aren't welcome at Danes' Dyke, never have been and never will be!' he informed her with relish. He advanced with measured tread towards the window and tugged a cord to swish back the curtains revealing windowpanes streaming with rain. 'Seems set for days,' he indicated with satisfaction. 'Your clothes are dry, I'll bring them up when I come back to fetch the tray.'

Raine bit into a piece of leathery toast and sipped slowly from a cup of tepid, milky tea. That she was unwelcome in this house was obvious, yet panic stirred within her at the thought of being turned away. She had no idea where she was or for what reason she had come, but instinctively she knew herself a stranger to the wild countryside she had traversed the previous night. Why else would she have kept expecting to see gently rolling hills replace the outcrops of grey granite or yearned to feel the caress of soft mist upon cheeks stung raw by driving rain? She choked on her toast when tears welled up and hastily she disposed of the tray in order to mop her eyes with a blue-ribboned, lace-trimmed cuff. *Women are not welcome at Danes' Dyke, never have been nor never will be!* Simeon's words seemed denied by the dainty femininity of her borrowed nightdress. Once, some woman had become ensconced deeply enough to have been allowed to deposit some of her belongings a woman, judging from her frivolous choice of night attire, who was as alien to this draughty house as she was herself!

She decided not to wait for Simeon's return, her luggage was bound to be about somewhere and a fresh change of clothing would help prop up her sagging spirits. After a short search she discovered a bathroom of sorts with antiquated fittings, pipes that chattered like machine-gun fire whenever she turned on taps that gushed icy water from out of corroded spouts.

She had a quick wash, then collided with Simeon when she left the bathroom clutching an eiderdown around her shivering limbs. He was carrying a pile of clothing which she recognized as her own, but her aversion to wearing unpressed articles wrinkled into a thousand creases was apparent when she glanced away from the bundle and stated definitely,

'I shan't be needing those, Simeon, I'll get fresh clothes from my suitcase, if you'll show me where it is?'

'Suitcase?' he repeated dourly. 'I've seen no suit-case.'

Her startled glance doubted his statement. 'But I must have a suitcase, how else would I carry my belongings?' she faltered, her brow puckering as she strove to pierce the veil clouding her mind.

'If you had any belongings to start with,' he sneered, flicking a contemptuous look over her dejected figure. 'We may be isolated on the moors, but we're not fools, you know! Every summer we're plagued with young tramps such as yourself who'd rather beg their way through life than lift a finger in honest toil. But Master Thor gives them short shrift, I can tell you,' he boasted proudly, 'he's got no time at all for beggars with hands white as driven snow!'

Instinctively, her fingers curled into a bunch to avoid examining eyes that were already fastened upon almond-shaped fingernails varnished iced-pink. With all the dignity she could muster, she defended, 'Though I have no idea who I am or where I came from, I feel certain I'm neither a tramp nor a beggar, merely an unfortunate person suffering a temporary lapse of memory. I'm sorry my stay has inconvenienced both you and your employer; as soon as I'm dressed I'll be on my way.'

As if to confound her brave statement, a rumble of thunder shook the house, rattling windows violently in their frames and causing floorboards to tremble beneath her feet. It came as no surprise when a tall figure loomed from out of nowhere: Thor, the master of Danes' Dyke, seemed at one with the element of thunder.

'You can't go just yet,' he clipped before Simeon could draw breath. 'Reluctant though I am to encourage your decadent mode of living, you cannot be allowed to risk crossing the moors when Nature is in such a violent mood. Look there,' with a brief nod he indicated the rainstreaked windows, 'it's barely noon, yet almost as dark as night.'

She followed his direction and shivered. The sky held a furious red tinge not unlike that she had glimpsed on her host's face the previous night. Outside, elements lay in wait for unsuspecting prey, while indoors resentment seethed behind the polite façade donned by the red-bearded giant whose green-flecked eyes were transmitting his dislike of feminine intrusion into his all-male domain.

'Get dressed!' She jerked to attention at his command. 'To be on the safe side, I've sent for Doctor Kendall, he'll be here soon to give you a check-up, so come downstairs when you're ready, don't keep him waiting!' As he strode off down the passageway she gaped at his retreating back. *Insufferable, domineering man!*

Simeon's self-satisfied expression was wiped clean at the sight of hauteur that had changed her delicate contours into a chiselled profile. 'Who do you think you are!' she heard him mutter as he brushed past her. 'I'm not impressed by your ladylike airs and graces!'

She returned to the bedroom carrying the bundle Simeon had thrust into her hands. Slowly she examined each article, searching for anything that might give some clue to her past. Items of underwear yielded only the brand name of a department store well known throughout the British Isles. Slacks, well-cut and of good material but showing signs of wear, gave away nothing of their place of origin and the hand-knitted jumper, though fashioned from thick, expensive wool, had no single characteristic to make it stand out from a hundred others.

She sank down on the bed, pressing her fingers hard against a pulse throbbing at her temple. There *had* to be a reason for her presence in this lonely place! Instinct warned her that she had been running away—but from what, from whom and why? Except for the memory of her encounter with her host on the rainswept moorland road her mind was a complete blank, but would he believe that, when at first sight he had labelled her shiftless? Even Simeon had practically accused her of lying in order to find a place to lay her head.

When she finished dressing she had to laugh at her mirrored reflection. Anyone less ladylike would be hard to imagine, she thought, remembering Simeon's accusation. Shrunken slacks stopped a good two inches above finely-boned ankles and her jumper was so stretched her outline could have been that of an undeveloped boy. Dark hair, raggedly cut, helped further the illusion. Puzzled, she groped behind her back just above the waist as if expecting to feel the stroke of silken tresses. A shadow darkened the brilliance of blue eyes as for a second the mist around her mind parted—she floundered, madly anxious to grasp an elusive memory floating just out of reach, but the mist thickened, leaving her mind blank and her body weak with fear.

Heeding her host's command, she hurried downstairs and was just in time to see Simeon ushering the doctor into a room leading off from the hall. She hurried after him, and was disconcerted to find her red-bearded host present and obviously prepared to remain during the examination which took the form of close questioning once the usual preliminaries of taking temperature and pulse rate had been concluded.

Doctor Kendall straightened his tie and began: 'Well, Miss——'

'Anonymous?' her host muttered from the depths of his beard.

The doctor ignored him and sent her a smile. 'Take no notice, my dear, Thor's bark is much worse than his bite, I assure you.' When she looked no less relieved, he sat next to her and coaxed, 'Try not to be afraid. Although distressing, amnesia is seldom lasting and provided you rest and try not to worry, pieces of your past will gradually be revealed to you until almost before you know it your mind's jigsaw will become complete.'

She was so relieved she clutched his hand. 'Then *you* believe me?' she trembled, holding her breath.

His eyebrows lifted. 'Why not, pray? Amnesia is not so unusual, more a common occurrence in these days of stress.'

Her glance flickered to her host, who was frowning. 'Rest and freedom from worry,' he quoted. 'And how will she obtain either, doctor, when the sum total of her possessions is the clothes she stands up in?'

'She could remain here,' he suggested mildly. 'I'm sure that after a few days' rest the young lady will not object to earning her keep.'

'That's out of the question!' Thor stood up, stretching intimidatingly tall.

But the doctor refused to be dominated. 'If you turn this girl away from the only surroundings with which she is familiar, then you must accept the blame for any tragic consequences,' he stated crisply. 'Come, Thor, reconsider,' he decided to employ reason against an outthrust chin, 'what possible harm could this infant wreck upon your male-dominated household? This place needs a woman's influence,' his glance around was derogatory, 'and so, too, does Vulcan, as I have so often reminded you.'

She wanted to run from the glowering giant whose look swivelled in her direction yet, perversely, she longed to be able to stay.

She held her breath as visibly he struggled with an urge to refuse, before unwillingly submitting.

'It seems I am left no choice,' his voice bit with aggravation. 'But heed this, Miss Anonymous, labour is a way of life to people who live on the moors and you'll be expected to work your passage. If the thought is discouraging, then I advise you to think carefully before deciding to stay!'

CHAPTER TWO

WHILE Thor showed the doctor out, Raine wandered around examining the many curious objects scattered around the room. They were predominantly nautical, models of old sailing ships, brass lamps, a selection of crudely fashioned tools of indeterminate use, and above the fireplace a long-handled, wickedly pointed lance hung aslant, as if the hand that had placed it there wished for a weapon permanently at the ready.

Hastily she transferred her attention to a table holding a scattering of intricately carved black figures. She was admiring a beautifully detailed stallion, mad-eyed, wild-maned, with front hooves poised ready to strike, when the deep-timbred voice of her host projected from the doorway.

'Sit down, Miss——' He checked himself impatiently. 'One of the many things which need to be established if you are to remain here is your name.'

'It's Raine, I'm certain of it.' She leant forward so eagerly she seemed in danger off falling off the edge of her seat.

Barely glancing her way, he sat down at a roll-topped desk and reached for a sheet of writing paper. With his back turned towards her she felt free to examine at will the broad expanse of shoulders stretching the width of a white, cable-patterned fisherman's jersey to capacity. His strength drew her like a magnet. In his presence she felt safe and secure and the inexplicable fear which so often rose up to threaten her was dispersed immediately he appeared.

'According to the doctor you have suffered some deep shock and your resulting amnesia is a form of defence, a mental mechanism engineered to blot out whatever fear is imprinted upon your mind. He assures me, however, that once your health improves and your confidence returns you will begin to recall small, seemingly unlinked incidents which might mean very little in isolation but which will eventually form a complete pattern. He suggests it might help if we keep a diary, jotting down any clues your subconscious may let slip about your old life while you are busy coping with the new.'

The dryness of his tone stung her almost to tears.

'You don't *really* believe I've lost my memory, do you, you're pretending just to humour me! Can't you take my word instead of harbouring the suspicion that you have a liar in your midst? Won't you at least give me the benefit of the doubt?'

When he pushed back his chair over bare floorboards the resulting noise grated raw across her nerves. She quivered, as with two giant strides he swallowed the gap between them and after a couple of quick gulps she obeyed his silent demand that she should meet his eyes. They were hard green stones, angry, implacable.

'All women are liars and cheats and without exception attempt to screen their hard hearts with soft words and pitiful looks,' he grated. 'Understand this—while you remain here you will be afforded none of the privileges your sex demand as a right. This is an all-male household and in order to retain the atmosphere I prefer I have given orders that you are to be treated as just another worker—no chivalrous offers to lighten your chores, no peacock preening to attract your favours. In fact, no disruption whatever of our usual routine! The farm workers have a midday meal in the kitchen each day except Sunday and you will join us there, rubbing elbow with grimy elbow and suppressing any inclination you might feel to turn up your nose at the smell of good honest sweat—is that clear?'

She exerted superhuman effort to suppress a very feminine desire to weep and supplied an answer with one nod of her shaggy head. Her eyes were downcast, so when his grim chuckle came surprise jolted through her body. She looked up, then quickly away to evade scornful eyes that missed not one wrinkle in her disreputable outfit.

'I don't know why I bothered the men with a warning lecture.' The indifference of his glance was degrading. 'They'll laugh their heads off when I present you in place of the siren they're probably expecting.'

Although hurt by his rough handling of her feelings, she felt no desire to retaliate. Instead pity stirred for the man whose animosity towards her sex obviously stemmed from some bitter experience that had left deep inward scars. Instinctively, she sensed hidden beneath his tough exterior a well of compassion channelled away from all members of her sex, present only for the benefit of those fortunate enough to be numbered among his friends.

She felt a sudden longing to be one of them!

Wisely, she hid the thought behind a tentative smile. 'Thank you so much for allowing me to stay, you're very kind.'

His red head jerked up, taken aback by her meek acceptance of all he had outlined. Beneath the beard his lips tightened with annoyance and his voice was brusque as he turned to walk back to his desk and demanded, 'We'll begin by cataloguing what little knowledge we have. Name: Raine— what a flight of fanciful nonsense!'

'No more fanciful than Thor, the Norse god of thunder,' she dared to defy.

He swung round to glare. 'My name is Torquil, a family name used by generations of Haldens. Many of the people along this coast are descended from Vikings who centuries ago came from across the sea to conquer. Many of them settled here and over the years much of their culture and many of their skills were absorbed by those with whom they came in contact. My own ancestors were ship-builders—the name Halden actually means "half Dane".'

She could not feign surprise when from the first moment of meeting she had likened him to a plundering Viking!

'And do you still build ships?' she questioned eagerly, fascinated by his glimpse into history.

'No, we do not.' Curtly he extinguished her curiosity and returned to the matter in hand. 'Judging from the state of your hands and the overall slightness of your limbs you're a stranger to manual work. Your clothing, good, but showing signs of wear, adds up to a liking for the expensive but a lack of sufficient funds with which to indulge your tastes. A certain grace of movement and an educated voice would seem to indicate that you might be a member of a somewhat impoverished family. Would you agree that assumption could be correct?' he snapped, swinging her a questioning look.

'I suppose so ... I'm not sure,' she gasped, wilting under the pressure of his dominance. She jumped to her feet, twisting agitated hands in a gesture of supplication. 'I would tell you if I could, but I honestly don't know, please believe ...' The floor heaved beneath her feet. She swayed and would have fallen had he not crossed swiftly to swing an arm around her waist.

'I'm sorry,' he apologized stiffly. 'We'll leave further questions until later.'

He guided her to a chair, then left her to tug savagely at a bell rope. Simeon's rapid answer to the summons brought a flicker of a smile to Raine's lips; the old man was so anxious to be rid of her he seemed always to be hovering in her vicinity expectant of hearing her commanded to leave. His dismay was visible when his master instructed, 'Fetch, Miss—Fetch Raine some tea, hot and strong —none of your lukewarm dishwater, mind—and be quick about it!' When Thor turned away Raine caught the full malevolence of Simeon's glare. She stared back, transfixed by the hatred on the old man's face, then as weakness swept over her she closed her eyes, nauseated by a feeling that once before she had experienced such a look, a look that had preceded a tragedy so horrible her mind had refused to retain its memory.

She was left alone in the dismal room to drink the tea—hot and strong as Thor had directed. Her hand shook as she lifted the heavy earthenware pot to pour out a cupful and a small click of annoyance escaped her when some of it spilled over into the saucer. She looked around, searching for something with which to mop up, and was startled almost out of her wits when she glimpsed a head rising slowly above the back of a sofa. For shocked seconds she stared at the face of a small boy whose solemn expression did not waver while he watched her struggle for composure.

'Who are you?' she finally managed to whisper.

'I'm Vulcan, and I don't need womanly 'fluence, like the doctor said, I don't need anybody but Thor, so go away, d'you hear, I don't want you here!'

Carefully she set down her cup. The boy was no more than five years old, red-haired and mutinous, and already showing signs of becoming as anti-feminist as his ... *father?* No wonder the doctor had voiced concern, the precocious child was obviously in need of a woman's care.

'Do you make a habit of eavesdropping on grown-ups' conversation?' she asked mildly, carefully avoiding a note of censure.

Defiantly, the boy stepped closer. 'It's the only way to find things out,' he admitted without shame, watching hopefully for signs of shock. 'Nobody tells me anything, but that doesn't stop me from finding out all I want to know!'

She disappointed him by remaining calm. 'But what if your father should find out, I imagine he would be extremely angry?'

For an instant he looked startled, then an impish grin split his face. 'He doesn't care what I do so long as I keep out of his way.'

There was a ring of truth about the statement and for the first time since her arrival she felt moved to anger. What sort of man was the master of Danes' Dyke? Already she knew him to be hard and insensitive in his dealings with her own sex, but to extend such feelings towards a child—his own child—was positively inhuman!

Conscious of his keen scrutiny, she made an effort to hide her indignation. 'Have some tea,' she almost pleaded, 'and tell me more about yourself.'

'I don't like tea,' he refused unblinkingly, 'but I'll talk to you for a while longer.'

'Thank you.' She had to strive not to sound too eager in case he should decide to cement the small crack in his reserve. Whether he would admit to it or not, the child was lonely, bored and starved of an interested audience. 'Tell me about the house,' she asked, once he had settled himself on the sofa.

'Danes' Dyke was built by my great-great—I'm not sure how many greats—grandfather Halden. He was a famous sea captain,' he boasted proudly, 'almost as famous as Captain Cook!' She nodded, looking suitably impressed. 'He hunted whales in the waters of Greenland and caught four times as many every trip than any other captain ever known. And not only did he have bigger catches,' he stressed what he had obviously heard stressed, 'but he always returned to port earliest and because of the freshness of the blubber his oil was always graded "best quality". Whale meat is called blubber,' he informed her kindly, 'did you know that?'

Daring herself to smile, she shook her head, crossing her fingers to cancel out the lie.

Looking satisfied, he continued, 'When he was very rich he retired from sailing and began building whalers, but after a while there were fewer and fewer whales because so many had been slaughtered and those that were left became scattered and were so rarely to be found that fishermen went for weeks without catching sight of one.' He sighed. 'That was when great ... grandfather Halden decided to build this house and farm the land. I do wish he hadn't,' he concluded wistfully, 'I'd much rather live aboard ship than on land and so would Thor, I know, 'cos I've heard him say so.'

She experienced such distaste at hearing him use his father's Christian name that her tone was sharper than she intended when she admonished. 'We can't have all things exactly as we would wish. Living on a farm can be fun, I love feeding chickens, milking cows, exercising the horses——' She stopped on a quickly-held breath, shaken by words that had tumbled glibly from her lips.

'Whoopee, you lived on a farm!' Vulcan scrambled from his seat and ran towards the desk. 'We must write that down, Thor said everything you remember must be entered in the diary!'

That first minor slip began a game Vulcan thoroughly enjoyed, his initial resentment forgotten as he shadowed her around the house, studying her as keenly as a specimen on a pin, sifting every innocent sentence for further clues to her past. At first he made her nervous, but gradually as she became used to being constantly shadowed she found his chatter amusing and was amazed at the amount of information the infant eavesdropper had managed to cull. Once she tried to remonstrate, knowing his father would be appalled by the boy's references to family affairs gleaned, she suspected from the blunt way in which they were framed, from the outspoken Simeon.

'You ought not to listen to servants' gossip,' she scolded. 'Your father would be very annoyed if he knew—both with yourself and with Simeon, who ought to know better than to discuss personal matters in the hearing of an inquisitive little boy.'

She wondered why he always betrayed small amusement, quickly marshalled behind a bland, poker-faced façade, whenever she referred to his father.

'Thor never gets annoyed with Simeon, they yarn together for hours about their sailing days and of how they long to get back to sea. Simeon's too old now, of course, but Thor could get command of a ship any time he liked if it weren't that he's tied here looking after me.'

They were walking towards the kitchen as he spoke and she halted in her tracks, stunned by the implied cruelty of his words. 'I'm sure you've misunderstood, Vulcan,' her voice wobbled as she met the child's wide, unblinking stare. 'People in a reminiscent mood might often seem to yearn for days past, but given the choice they seldom choose to

26

pull up their roots. I'm certain that however much your father loves the sea he much prefers living here with you.'

'That's silly!' he scoffed, rounding on her like a miniature tornado. 'All Halden men have salt water in their veins, Simeon says so! One day, I'll sail to Greenland, just like Great-great-grandfather Halden did, and I'll bring back hundreds of whales! But,' the darkness of the passage they had just entered seemed to absorb a small sob, 'I've got to grow up first and that takes ever such a long time...!' She dared not attempt to comfort the sturdy little individual, but as her footsteps slowed, allowing him time to compose himself before they entered the kitchen, tears pricked behind her eyelids and her own troubles faded as she pondered on how best to penetrate the shell of hurt gathered around the heart of a child.

As she pushed open a green baize door the contrasting brightness of the kitchen made her blink. Outside, the storm had abated and weak sunshine was penetrating the huge room, playing upon glistening copper pans hung around colour-washed walls, upon a table and benches scrubbed so thoroughly the grain of the wood stood bared, and upon a red-tiled floor so spotless Raine felt loath to set foot upon its surface.

Vulcan had no such inhibitions, he left her hesitating on the threshold and ran to greet his father who, accompanied by his farm workers, had begun filing into the kitchen through an outside door. Seven men took their places around the table, Thor, Simeon and five workmen, and as they all, after the curtest of nods, ignored her presence and proceeded to eat, she felt herself an outcast from male society.

Covertly she studied them as food was handed around the table, forced, by lack of introductions, to name each one secretly in her mind. The youngest, a lad of about seventeen who looked as if he had spent the night outdoors, she christened Sleepy; Simeon fell naturally for the title of Grumpy and when, to her secret amusement, one man sneezed as his grinning companion waved the pepper pot under his nose, they were immediately dubbed Sneezy and Happy. Thor she did not attempt to caricature, his conflicting roles of ogre and protector defied description!

Few words were spoken as crisply-roasted potatoes, stewed steak and vegetables were quickly demolished to make way for slices of sponge pudding smothered in custard, then, obviously replete, the men gathered up mugs of tea and began making their way into a rest room set apart from the kitchen. Simeon made to follow them, and as he passed Raine tentatively offered, 'You're an excellent cook, Simeon, the meal was delicious! Don't hurry back, I'll do the washing up.'

She shuddered with shock when he spat angrily. 'You'll do no such thing! I'll have no woman interfering in my kitchen!'

'But I . . .' Her protest died as he stumped away, resentment in every stiff step.

Calmly stuffing the bowl of his pipe with tobacco, Thor explained, 'In this kitchen Simeon reigns supreme, just as he did in the galley aboard

28

ship. The rest of the house is top-heavy with dust, as you may already have noticed, but all Simeon cares about is his kitchen. Please don't try to encroach upon his territory, I value my digestion too highly to risk having him upset.'

'I only wanted to help,' she gasped, still reeling from the onslaught of the old man's resentment.

'Can't you dust or something?' Vaguely he waved his pipe through the air. 'Or if you feel up to it you might try keeping Vulcan out of my hair. When the weather improves get him to show you around, take him to the coast—he'll spend hours just hanging around the harbour.'

'Rain used to live on a farm!' Vulcan's small voice piped from nowhere. 'We discovered that this morning and entered it straight into the diary, just as you said.'

Raine jerked upright; at times the boy withdrew so quietly into his shell one was apt to forget he was there.

Curiously, Thor studied her flushed face. 'Discovered. . . ?' he murmured, then waited with eyebrows uplifted.

'I happened to remember that I like feeding chickens,' she stumbled, feeling somehow bound to plead her case, 'and exercising horses . . .'

'Interesting!' he drawled. 'I wish I'd been present to decide for myself whether the information was the result of jolted memory or, what seems more likely, an unthinking slip of the tongue!'

CHAPTER THREE

AFTER a few days the weather improved to such an extent Raine felt it would be criminal to remain indoors. During their enforced captivity she and Vulcan had explored the house thoroughly, dusting and cleaning as they went until, although still far from perfect, the rooms were respectable enough to be left unattended until more time was made available by a further spell of bad weather.

Their most promising discovery was a mini-car found tucked away in one of the outhouses, three of which had been converted into garages. One housed Thor's Range Rover, the second was empty and in the third, covered by a tarpaulin, was a small red car which, judging from its appearance, had lain dormant for quite some time. As soon as she saw it she felt confident she could drive, but the urge to experiment was frustrated by the absence of the ignition key necessary to start up the engine. Nothing would have induced her to approach Thor. Something about the abandoned car seemed to indicate that it had been bought for the use of a woman—his wife, perhaps—and the thought of reviving memories of the woman who was either dead or had deserted Vulcan and his father was repugnant to her.

'Simeon will have the key, shall I ask him for it?' Vulcan offered, hopping from one foot to the other, his eyes shining at the prospect of widening horizons.

'He could do no worse than refuse, I suppose,' she acceded, doubtful of meeting with co-operation from the surly old man.

As Vulcan ran off towards the kitchen, she slid into the driver's seat, feeling mounting confidence as instinctively she carried out the operation of engaging gear. She was fiddling happily with the various knobs and switches when Vulcan reappeared dragging a grumbling Simeon behind him.

'It'll take me all day to get that toy fit for the road,' he glared. 'It must be all of five years since it was last used.'

'You mean you'll do it?' She could hardly believe her ears.

'It's a shame to see it fall into disuse,' he muttered, running a thorny hand across the bonnet. 'I've maintained it as best I could, but it needs an outing as much as the boy does.' She warmed to the hint of softening. The old man hid his fondness for the child well, but beneath an abrupt manner was hidden concern for his welfare.

Taking care not to show too much enthusiasm, she turned to walk away, casting across her shoulder. 'It would be nice to go for a drive, especially now the weather is so good. I believe the coast is a mere half hour's drive across the moor? Such a pity to be marooned here—Vulcan adores the sea, he's always prattling on about the lighthouse and the harbour ...'

She willed Vulcan not to mention the car to Thor when they dined together that evening. It was foolish, she knew, but she had no intention of being forbidden to take out the car because of a licence she felt sure she owned but could not produce. A car represented freedom of a sort, and if by chance Vulcan should mention any of their proposed outings to his father she was counting on lack of interest leading him to assume that they were to travel by bus.

Excitement was intense when next morning after breakfast Simeon dourly informed them that the car was fit for the road, with a full fuel tank and even a flask of lemonade and a packet of sandwiches in the boot. Raine, almost as delighted as Vulcan, tried to show her appreciation, but her thanks were brushed aside. 'I did it for the boy, not for you! See you take care of him, and mind you're back in time for dinner!' Grateful that his simple reasoning had not stretched so far as to question her ability to drive, she beat a hasty retreat from the kitchen feeling happier than she had done since her arrival at Danes' Dyke.

The road was an extension of the grey ribbon she had travelled on the day of her arrival, but as the little car purred across its surface Raine felt she was in a different world. The moors were bathed in sunshine, and for miles as far as the eye could see sheep grazed contentedly beneath a sky of cloudless, brilliant blue. It was still possible to remember, however—as they sped straight as an arrow in the direction of the ancient seaport that in days gone by had owed much of its prosperity to Vulcan's ancestors—that once the road they were travelling had been no more than a rough moorland track, so sparsely signposted by stones and crosses that only the bravest and most determined travellers had remained undeterred.

She smiled to herself when Vulcan began fidgeting with excitement, sensing that they were nearing their destination, but her own pleasure was no less than his when unexpectedly they breasted a rise and there beneath them, nestling within a crooked arm of cliff, lay a picturesque harbour enclosed by tiers of narrow streets rising so steeply upwards that shops and houses appeared to be clinging precariously to the towering cliffs.

'The fishing fleet is in!' Vulcan's voice was pitched high with excitement. 'Please, can we go straight to the harbour?'

'Of course,' she laughed, 'I can hardly wait to be shown around!'

Feeling inordinately proud of her skill and road-sense, she manoeuvred the car through narrow, busy streets until they reached a car park near the harbour, then filled with a spirit of adventure the earlier Haldens might have envied, they set off walking, drawn like magnets towards the line of masts strung out along the quay.

To her surprise, Vulcan seemed well-known to the fishermen who welcomed him with huge grins and greeted him by name, 'Well, young feller, come to pester us again, have you?' one black-jerseyed sailor teased.

'I've come to show my friend around, Skipper Postgate,' he replied with grown-up dignity. 'Do you mind if we stand here and watch you unload the catch?'

'Bless you, no!' The skipper's twinkling eyes contrasted brilliantly against his tan. 'Better than that, come aboard, I'll find you a seat where you can see everything without getting in the way!'

Eagerly they scrambled over the side and felt enormously privileged when they were ensconced on a pile of upturned boxes and left with the strict injunction not to move until the skipper gave permission.

'We won't, I promise you,' Raine's husky voice assured him as he prepared to resume his duties, 'and thank you, Skipper Postgate, for your kindness.'

'There's not much we fishermen wouldn't do for Captain Halden, lad,' he replied gruffly. 'Keeping an eye on his charges is little enough return for all he's done for us.' Vulcan stifled a giggle but did not give her away. In her shapeless jumper, creased jeans and with hair short and unkempt anyone could be forgiven for mistaking her for a boy.

'*Captain* Halden?' When the skipper had gone curiosity prompted the question. 'The skipper referred to your father as *Captain* Halden, is it a courtesy title, do you suppose?'

Vulcan tore his eyes away from the fascinating scene just long enough to scoff, 'Of course not. I've already explained that Thor gave up command of his ship to look after me!'

Some of her puzzlement disappeared as she began to understand her host and the heartache such a decision must have caused him. He belonged to the sea, was as much part of it as the wind, the rain and the other more violent element from which he took his name. She pictured him as she had so often seen him, striding the passages of the old house as if they were open decks, swinging on his heel with restrained savagery each time his progress was blocked by a brick wall, then striding off in the opposite direction, chin outthrust, rebelling inwardly against the absence of wind and biting spray. Abrupt and uncaring though he might seem, he had accepted the ultimate sacrifice of giving up the life he loved in order to ensure the welfare of his small son!

Vulcan interrupted her train of thought with information he was bursting to air. 'Do you know the names of all those fish?' He pointed downward to where the catch was stacked in boxes ready to be winched ashore.

'I do!' he claimed hastily when her lips framed a reply. 'The main catch is cod, with a few haddock, whiting and skate and those flat fish are plaice. This boat is a keel boat, you see,' his bright head glistened in the sunshine as he nodded towards fishing nets swaying in the breeze. 'They use several types of net—trawl, seine, drift and line, and two of the smaller keel boats fish for crab and lobster all the year round.'

She did not need to pretend to be impressed. 'How come you know so much, did Simeon teach you?'

'Simeon and Thor both told me a little,' he confessed, 'but a lot I picked up for myself just by listening to the fishermen. Come on,' he scrambled from his seat as the last box of fish was being winched on to the quayside, 'I'll show you the crabs and lobsters now.' Mindful of the skipper's warning, she put out a detaining hand, but then out of the corner of her eye she saw a wave from the wheelhouse, indicating that it was safe for them to make their way ashore.

An auction was in full swing when they reached the fish quay, so they joined the buyers, stepping over gushing hosepipes to inspect the wriggling harvest reaped only hours earlier, and watching with keen interest the swinging needle registering the weight of fish being quickly slung on and off a huge weighing scale. 'Isn't it *exciting*!' Vulcan whispered, his hot, sticky fingers reaching out unthinkingly to capture her hand. Her heart faltered, then raced on. Was this small gesture destined to be her one and only victory over the male occupants of Danes' Dyke, or could it be an indication that her presence might, in time, be found tolerable? Her delight in such a prospect found expression in a quick squeeze of the small hand nestling inside her own, but her smile faltered when, as if suddenly reminded that she was to remain an outcast, he withdrew contact and thrust his suddenly clenched fist deep into his pocket.

She tried not to show how much the action had hurt, but it was difficult to recapture the air of easy companionship they had earlier shared, and a lump in her throat kept her silent while Vulcan explained in detail the habits and characteristics of lobster and crab. She shivered with apprehension when he picked up a crab with claws still threshing.

'This one is female,' he astounded her by saying.

'The male is heavier, with a larger apron, but the female's flesh is much more succulent.'

As they moved on, Raine swallowed her hurt and attempted to revive the flagging conversation. 'All the lobsters I've seen have been red, how come these are dark blue?'

His upraised eyebrows were miniature replicas of Thor's. 'Because they aren't cooked yet,' he scoffed, then, dormant devilry aroused, he decided to shock. 'They're thrown into cauldrons of boiling water while they're still alive!'

Her stomach heaved and she experienced sudden aversion to the young monster with an inherited tendency to enjoy deliberate cruelty. She turned away from him, trembling, as a spectre from the past pounded upon the locked door of her mind, a spectre resurrected by a child's expression of sadistic enjoyment...

She was leaning against the harbour wall fighting a puzzling faintness when she heard Vulcan's voice as if from afar. 'There's Thor's Range Rover, he must be inside the Shipping Office—I'll go and see!'

'No!' Her hastily whispered denial did not reach the boy's ears and with a sense of foreboding she watched his small figure running in the direction of a wooden building set at the far end of the quay. When he had climbed up a flight of steps and disappeared through a doorway, she utilized the following minutes to regain her composure, hoping fervently that the child was mistaken—one Range Rover looked very much like another and Vulcan had barely given himself time to check the number plate. But the hope died a sudden death when an unmistakable figure appeared at the doorway through which Vulcan had disappeared and halted at the top of the flight of steps to scan the crowd below.

For seconds she watched him unobserved, thinking, as the sun struck his fiery head, that this was how the first Halden must have looked as he stood upon the bridge of a whaler searching the ocean for the first sight of prey. She flinched when she was caught in his sights, harpooned by piercing eyes that forbade her to move as he began striding her way. She waited, mesmerized, breaking from his glance only when he had drawn near enough to cast a shadow across her pale face.

'Vulcan tells me you drove here by car—I'd like a more detailed explanation.'

Inwardly she cringed, but she tried to reason with the owner of the grim voice. 'We discovered the car in the garage and asked Simeon to make it serviceable. I . . . I thought it a good idea to remove Vulcan and myself as far as possible from the house . . . we seem always to be in the way.'

'And your loss of memory had no effect upon your ability to drive?' he scathed, 'nor caused you any misgivings as to whether or not you're competent to drive a strange car through strange surroundings?'

'None,' she answered truthfully. 'I think I must have used a similar type of car—I felt at home immediately I sat behind the wheel—and I read the road quite well.' Pride in her achievement enabled her to look him straight in the eye. 'I coped without difficulty even through the town,' she boasted, then faltered, wondering if storm signals were green.

'So.' At the sound of sarcasm she braced herself. 'You *suspected* you could drive; you felt *at home* behind the wheel, you *read* a perfectly straight road, and on the strength of that you decided to put both Vulcan's life and your own at risk!'

'Oh, no!' she gasped. 'I would never——'

'But you already have,' he rasped, controlling his aggravation with difficulty. 'How can you be certain that you would have reacted properly in the event of an emergency? Your confidence could easily stem from a few hours' tuition as a learner driver, did you think of that? When you can show me a licence I'll believe you competent, but until then you're not to drive the car again, especially not with Vulcan as a passenger!'

She wanted to argue, but honesty forced her to accept that what he had said was true. He was not a man to trust to hunches, always he would need to be certain, to have suspicions confirmed or denied so that no room was left for doubt. A stubborn, immovable man, yet one upon whose integrity and strength she was glad to lean.

'I'm sorry,' she offered, her shorn head drooping on her slender neck. 'Of course you're right.'

Far from mollifying him the admission seemed to provoke even more anger. His huge frame stiffened and his hand curled into a clenched fist as if to control an urge for violence. 'If you remain with us long enough you'll discover I'm always right,' he informed her icily. 'Up until recently my home has

39

been run on the lines of a ship, efficiently and harmoniously, and as long as I'm in command I'll allow no insubordination below deck, is that understood?'

Her blood ran cold. For Vulcan's sake she had to protest. 'You surely don't subject a young boy to such harsh discipline? Children need to be loved, Captain Halden, don't you realize that? Think of your own childhood, remember your mother and the love she must have poured out on you, then perhaps you'll begin to understand Vulcan's needs and try to supply some of the things he has missed.'

When she dared to look up his eyes were cold as ice floes upon Arctic seas.

'I never knew my mother—just as Vulcan has never known his. Life at Danes' Dyke was too comfortless for either of them, they both stayed only long enough to give sons to the men they married before deserting to the towns from which they came. My father was a stricter disiplinarian than I, yet I survived and so too will Vulcan, *without* spurious sentiment or sympathy. He will be taught, as I was, that women are superfluous to requirements, necessary only if one wishes to propogate the species . . .'

She was directed to sit in the back of the Range Rover on the drive home—put in her place—relegated to the position of least importance by the man whose scorn of her sex stemmed from bitter seeds sown in his mind while still a boy. She felt anger against his father, the man whose bitterness he had inherited and which even now was being passed on to ensure a third generation of woman-hating Haldens, and against his wife who, however much deprived, had had no right to desert her infant son. Her worried eyes were drawn towards Vulcan, but she had to admit as she listened to his cheerful prattle that outwardly, at least, he was showing no sign of deprivation. Yet instinctively she knew that behind the male arrogance set so incongruously upon young shoulders was hidden a yearning to which the boy could probably put no name—a need for soft words of comfort to heal a bruised knee, or a tender goodnight kiss in place of the usual brusque command that he should retire to bed. She stirred uncomfortably. Thor's methods were wrong, too criminally harsh, so—and her pulses raced at the thought—she knew she was committed to pointing out to him once more the error of his ways.

CHAPTER FOUR

DURING the following weeks the opportunity Raine sought eluded her. Thor, she discovered, spent most of his time at the harbour, looking after the interests of the fishermen and their dependants or just generally messing about with boats. Whether this state of affairs had arisen only since her arrival she had no means of knowing, but Simeon's deepening resentment made her suspect that Thor's prolonged absences were being accounted her fault, with consequent black marks notched up against her.

The loneliness of her existence, coupled with the blankness of a mind which no amount of probing could penetrate, ought to have left her depressed, but she was strangely content to remain an outcast and her obvious happiness as she went about her chores cast sunshine into every corner of the house and coaxed slow, warming response from the men, responses which at first took the form of hesitant grins whenever she appeared, then graduated from shy greetings to covert acts of kindness such as the saddling of a horse whenever she wanted to ride, swift offers to help lift heavy carpets on to the lawn for cleaning, or the carrying of buckets of distemper with which she had transformed almost every room. Vulcan, too, became her shadow as each day was turned into an adventure, each chore an exciting exploit. He maintained his reserve, but she felt amply rewarded by his reaction to her casual suggestion.

'I think you're old enough to learn to ride, don't you? How about asking the foreman, Mr Marshall, to pick you out a suitable pony?'

Pop-eyed with delight, he breathed, 'But who'll teach me? Thor says I'm not old enough yet to match my strength against a pony, and Simeon doesn't ride.'

'I'll teach you,' she twinkled, her eyes deeply blue. 'If you'll allow me to, that is?'

Swallowing back delighted acceptance, he strove to sound indifferent. 'All right, I don't mind being taught by a woman, just to begin with.'

Controlling an urge to turn him on her knee and deliver a good spanking, she allowed the insult to pass. 'Good, then there's no time like the present, let's go down to the stables.'

Ted Marshall was most co-operative. Waving towards a nearby field containing half a dozen dales ponies, he offered, 'Take your pick, Miss Raine, I'm sure you can judge horseflesh as well as anyone. After watching you ride and hearing you use words that are everyday terms to horsemen I'm convinced you've forgotten more about horses than most of us around here have ever known.'

She flushed with pleased surprise—his keen look after a previous request for a curry-comb to help remove dirt and hairs from grooming brushes was now fully explained. 'Strange,' she mused, 'but I've a feeling you're right. I do know about horses, without even thinking I've saddled, ridden and groomed them, yet for the life of me I can't remember where...'

'Give yourself time, Miss Raine,' Ted Marshall urged kindly, 'don't try to hurry nature, your memory will return soon enough—too soon, perhaps,' he muttered awkwardly, 'my wife was saying only the other day how much happier Master Vulcan seems since your arrival here.'

'Thank you. Ted.' She felt warmed by his shy praise. 'I feel so useless sometimes, it's good to know I'm not entirely unappreciated.'

Her small conquest lent added spring to her step as, with Vulcan at her heels, she approached the grazing ponies. Expertly she sized them up, then moved without hesitation towards a placid, aged pony, reasonably thin without being narrow-chested, with a not too long back and well-rounded quarters. His coat was black, and a shaggy fringe fell across large, soulful eyes that questioned without panic when she reached out to stroke him.

'This is the one for you,' she decided. 'What shall we call him?'

Her spirits sank when she glanced down at his mutinous face. 'That one is too old. Thor will laugh at me if I sit astride that old rocking horse! I want a younger one.'

Patiently she explained, 'One of the most important qualities of a pony for a beginner is that it should have a good temperament, be obedient, and neither be inclined to try to get you off its back by rearing or bucking, nor bolt with you. These qualities are attained only by ponies fairly well on in years. This one has all its youthful over-playful-

44

ness out of its system and will be content to carry out its duties undisturbed by noises that might excite a younger pony.'

Anxiously she waited for the cloud to lift from his face, taking heart from the lessened heat of his protest. 'I'll look silly riding that old thing...!'

'But he's a beautiful pony!' she argued, then deciding upon a change of tactics she capitulated. 'If, after the first few lessons, you still aren't happy with him I promise we'll change to one a little more adventurous, is that agreed?'

His red head flashed fire in the sunlight as he nodded vigorous agreement. 'Very well—and I think I'll call him Son of Lucifer, just because he's small there's no reason why he shouldn't be given a big name.'

Son of Lucifer, shortened after a while to the more affectionate if not strictly accurate Luci, became the love of Vulcan's life. Each morning before breakfast he sped down to the stables to muck out, feed and water Luci, all the while carrying on a conversation in a low undertone, spilling out confidences that reached only the animal's uppricked ears. In fact, the bond between boy and pony became so marked that Raine began to worry and tried to protect the boy from the heartache of losing a beloved pet by attempting to get him to share some of his affection with another younger pony. But he remained aloof, determined that nothing and no one would come between himself and his beloved friend.

Unfortunately, from the very first riding lesson, he showed a strong aversion to wearing a hard hat.

Firmly Raine insisted upon his wearing the protective headgear, but his reluctant obedience became wearing in the extreme. As she was walking down to the paddock where both he and the pony were waiting to begin a lesson, she faltered with a weary sigh, noting that once again the despised hat had been slung into a corner of the paddock.

'Please fetch your hat and put it on, Vulcan,' she insisted without heat, prepared for a battle to begin.

He remained seated in the saddle, his back rigid. 'Hats are for cissies. I'm not likely to fall off, I never do ...'

'There has never been a rider who hasn't fallen off some time or another!' she reminded him sharply, 'but what is equally important, the hat is also meant as protection from low branches.'

Haughtily, he glanced around. 'There are none here in the paddock,' he argued with an insolent gleam, feeling himself triumphing in the battle of wills.

Before she could muster a reply, a cold command was aimed from across her shoulder. 'Dismount immediately, go to your room, and stay there until I give you my permission to leave!'

Raine stiffened, dreading the consequences of disobedience, then felt even more apprehensive when, after a second's hesitation, the boy slid wordlessly from the saddle and stalked angrily away.

'Come to my study, there's something we must discuss,' Thor directed, his cold voice sending shivers down her spine. Wordlessly, she followed him into the house and waited while he paced the study, noting his wrinkled brow and the deepening green of his eyes. The silence lasted so long her thoughts began to wander: What sort of face lay behind the screening red beard? Arrogant, no doubt, with a chin firmly jutting to match the stern outline of a mouth chipped from granite and a formidable profile to match the giant frame that generated so much power and assurance.

So deeply preoccupied had she become, she gave a nervous jump when he rounded swiftly and pounced. 'I will not allow you to mollycoddle Vulcan, d'you hear? Of late he's become petted, inclined to sulkiness when crossed and very much slower to obey orders. You're to blame for this change—you've fussed over him like a broody hen ever since you arrived here, given in to his every whim, coaxed, cajoled and cosseted him to such an extent he is within an ace of becoming a spoilt, impudent and wilfully disobedient brat!'

His attack took her so much by surprise she could project no more than a gasp through parted lips.

'Don't bother to deny it!' he growled in a tone that would have subdued a pack of mutineers. 'Fortunately, I've recognized the danger soon enough to prevent you causing any permanent damage, but in future you will keep your distance, at no time are you and the boy to spend time alone together, and as a punishment for the display of tantrums I witnessed earlier he'll be told that the stables are out of bounds until further notice.'

'You can't!' Her shocked whisper was a mere thread of sound. 'Not even you could be so cruel!

Punish me if you must—though for what crime I have no idea—but please don't deprive the boy of his only outlet of affection. Luci means more to him than any living creature, you wouldn't ... you *can't* inflict such suffering upon a child!'

Green eyes flashed and nostrils flared while her distracted eyes roved his features, searching desperately for a hint of softening. 'I shall use whatever method I think best to eliminate the unfortunate traits you've fostered in the boy's character. I do not wish to discuss the subject further—my orders have been clearly outlined, see to it that they are obeyed promptly and to the letter!'

Picturing the boy's reaction to being parted indefinitely from his pet was unbearably distressing. Raine clenched her fists and swallowed deeply before choking out, 'You're carrying the fantasy of living life aboard ship to extremes, Captain Halden! Danes' Dyke as a home is far from perfect, but fortunately, as it's the only one Vulcan has ever known, he's unable to draw comparisons!' She tensed her slight body to combat his look of hauteur, and forced herself to pour further scorn upon his methods. 'What will you do to me if I refuse to obey your orders, Captain? Have me tied to the mast and flogged, or taken below and put in irons? I wouldn't put either past you,' she shakily admitted. 'Your resentment of the wife who deserted you has developed into a misguided hatred of all women that has grown to such proportions it now encompasses children—even your own son!'

A dreadful silence fell, a silence so complete that the ticking of a brass ship's clock hung just above the fireplace filled every corner of the room strewn with relics of bygone whaling days. Small wonder I'm not allowed in here even to dust, she fretted while she waited with head downcast to be reprimanded; of all the rooms in the house, this, the captain's den, was the most aggressively masculine.

Predictably, his answer when it came was lance-sharp. 'Like all women, you're quick to jump to wrong conclusions. I have no wife, and Vulcan is not my son!'

'Not ...?' Her blue eyes reflected puzzlement. 'But Vulcan has often referred to you as his father?'

'Then the boy is a liar!'

'No, I must have ... misunderstood,' she stammered, recalling the child's wicked delight in teasing and the amusement she had afforded him whenever she had rebuked him for using his father's Christian name. Colour rushed to her cheeks as his unkind glance swept her embarrassed face; she felt deserving of the contempt he obviously had for her very feminine reasoning.

He flicked her a look that stung before striding towards the window to train far-sighted mariner's eyes upon rolling hills, dipping and heaving like a sea of petrified waves. 'My family's affairs are none of your business, but to avoid further faulty conjecture on your part, I'd better explain. Vulcan is my brother's child,' he informed her austerely, without turning his head. 'Britt, my twin, has always been an impulsive devil, even as a child he was for ever in trouble with our father for insubordination. Whichever rule he disagreed with he simply ignored, with dire consequences. We

49

were none of us surprised when, during his early days at a naval training establishment, he became involved with a girl who, after a ridiculously short courtship, became his wife. Vulcan is the only good that came of that disastrous alliance. As the girl had no close relatives she stayed here at Danes' Dyke until her child was born, then a few weeks later, after a storming row with Britt, she returned to the city for which she was pining, leaving Britt and the baby without a qualm. Naturally, divorce proceedings were instituted, but before they were finalized our father died. Britt stayed only until after the funeral, then he, too, disappeared leaving a note stating he needed breathing space, time to think, before deciding what was to be done about his son.

'That was the last I heard from him,' he concluded, his voice shocking in its grimness. Then quietly, speaking almost to himself, she heard him went on, 'According to my father, Britt took after our mother—the wife he had sworn to hate—yet I always felt that of the two of us Britt was his favourite...'

Raine's heart jolted, glimpsing the hurt behind the whispered words, words that betrayed the bewilderment of a youth who had modelled himself upon a father he worshipped only to discover that the brother whose lesser qualities he had often heard scorned had somehow stolen the affection he himself had craved. He would have scoffed had he known how deeply she was touched on his behalf, her pity was so fierce she felt it as a physical pain— never again would she tremble before his piercing eyes nor be cowed by his powerful roar. Thor, the intimidating giant, had once been and could be again—vulnerable to love!

With difficulty she husked a question past a lump in her throat. 'So you sacrificed your own career in order to bring up Vulcan, allowed your brother to unload his responsibilities, left him free to pursue his own pleasures?'

The still figure stirred, then after slight hesitation replied without heat, 'Britt, although frivolous in outlook, inherited much of our ancestors' flair for seamanship. Few can equal his skill as a navigator, even as a cadet he showed such outstanding promise that his superiors had no hesitation in forecasting a brilliant career. One can hardly blame him for striving to ensure his talents were not wasted.'

'But what about your talents?' she argued fiercely, blinking back tears pricking behind her eyelids. 'I refuse to believe, Captain Halden, that they are any less than your brother's ... you're too modest ... too kind...' As her voice broke so did the dam of tears brought into being by her new, deeper insight into the character of this giant with the gentle heart.

She heard his gasp of amazement as he swung away from the window and feeling swamped by waves of embarrassment she fumbled in her pockets for a handkerchief in order to avoid meeting his incredulous look. When a white square of linen was thrust under her nose she grasped it with an incoherent murmur of thanks.

'Tears? For me ...?'

She looked up and saw that he was nonplussed, struggling to restore the shell that had cracked under the pressure of a woman's tears. No one had ever cried on his behalf, she realized with a jolt. No one had ever taken the trouble to care about the neglected boy grown into an even more solitary man.

'I'm sorry,' she jerked, controlling an errant sob, 'you must think me a fool. It's just that it all seems so *wrong*! Why should you suffer the price of your brother's misdemeanours? Your happiness is every bit as important as his.'

He rocked on his heels, surprised by her vehemence, then before her astonished eyes his face became transformed by a slow smile that bared a flash of white teeth and which for a moment even reached his eyes, adding a softening glow to their usual biting gleam.

'Thank you for thinking so.' He did not unbend far enough to relinquish his clipped coolness, but nevertheless she felt a glow of warmth that had nothing to do with the mildness of the day. Curbing a shocking impulse to embrace the tall, solitary man, she waited, afraid to speak in case words should shatter the calm of the first understanding moment they had ever shared. Her diplomacy did not go unrewarded. 'Perhaps I have been a little harsh on the boy,' his voice grated on the unwilling admission. Then hesitantly, the words were torn out of him. 'The house has been much more cheerful since you came—brighter, somehow.' He waved a vague hand. 'Fires lighted on chilly evenings, splashes of colour in dark corners, the gleam of polished wood . . .' He stopped, looking slightly uncomfortable at having betrayed such sentiments, but he had said enough to erase the memory of all the back-breaking labour she had expended, all the more tiring because she had thought the results ignored.

'I like housework,' she smiled, dwarfed by the massive-shouldered, lean-hipped giant within whose shadow she felt safe and protected.

'Strange girl.' She loved his slow, grave smile. 'Britt's wife hated it, she said it roughened her hands and split her nails. My mother was also reputed to be very much averse to such chores.'

She dared an opinion to which she had given much thought. 'I think both your father and your brother must have been either very thoughtless or else lacking in judgement. After all, who in his right mind would expect a hot-house plant to survive conditions on an open moor? Is it so surprising that women reared on the pleasures of city life should rebel against the totally different life style of the country? Mariners have a reputation of being far-sighted, deep-thinking men,' she concluded, 'yet your father and brother both, it seems to me, were unable to see beyond a pretty face.'

She had transgressed, she realized; immediately his expression changed to one of deep distaste. His loyalty was such that he was not yet ready to hear his family disparaged.

'I can't deny that you may be right, but I do deny you the right to express such an opinion,' he rebuked her coldly. Swiftly he withdrew, turning his back on the boyish, tangled-haired figure with the distressed face, and flung a dismissal across his shoulder. 'Vulcan will no doubt be waiting to learn his fate. As my previous orders have already been retracted you don't need my permission to go to him!'

CHAPTER FIVE

As if ashamed of his small interlude of weakness, Thor became even more unapproachable during the days that followed, remaining reserved and silent during the rare times he was present to share their meals. Vulcan, however, as if sensing an escape from near-disaster, became more biddable and as the riding lessons progressed his piping laughter was heard rising more and more often from the direction of the paddock. As his enjoyment grew so did his affection for Luci, and feeling very much shut out Raine suffered small pangs of envy as she was relegated to the edge of the magic circle she so yearned to share. On odd occasions, the prematurely-mature infant forgot his dignity and relaxed his guard. Those moments—always surprising—were infinitely sweet.

They were sauntering back to the house after a particularly enjoyable session with Luci when, during a spate of animated conversation, Vulcan reached out to slip small, sweaty fingers into her palm. Tentatively, she responded by tightening her grasp and when his fingers were not withdrawn she smiled down at the freckled urchin with the large, earnest eyes and a shock of startling hair.

'It's very good of you to teach me to ride,' he admitted gruffly. 'I don't think you are a hippy or a tramp, and if you were as lazy as Simeon says you wouldn't bother to do any work at all—especially not housework.'

'Simeon still doesn't trust me, does he?' she murmured wryly, hurt by the old man's stubborn refusal to accord her any virtues.

'No,' he answered truthfully, wrinkling his nose, 'but you needn't worry about the things he says, no one really believes you're out to sink claws into Thor—anyway, as Mr Mitchell pointed out, Thor's not the marrying kind . . .'

Her gasp of indignation was drowned by the roar of a powerful engine. They both halted, conversation forgotten as they digested the unusual sight of a sleek car crammed with luggage racing up the drive. 'Who can that be?' she wondered aloud, feeling unreasonably apprehensive.

'Probably tourists,' Vulcan shrugged. 'We often get them coming to the door asking for directions.'

But when they eventually rounded the corner of the house and reached the car they found it was deserted. Luggage was still piled in the back, but both the driver's and passenger's seats were empty. Then from inside the house they heard a voice, familiar yet unfamiliar, deep-timbred yet registering an unusual amount of amusement.

'The old place hasn't changed one bit—a little tidier, perhaps, but still retaining every iota of its forbidding grimness! Can you feel it, my love, that atmosphere of prudish uptightness that first drove us away?'

A tinkling laugh reached their ears. 'Indeed I can,' a woman's voice answered, 'but thank heaven, this time we're not obliged to stay.'

When the voices moved out of earshot they remained rooted to the spot, digesting the information that had unwittingly come their way.

'Was it Thor, do you think?' Vulcan faltered. 'It sounded just like him, yet...'

'No,' Raine stated with conviction. 'The voice was Thor's, but the sentiments and the way which they were expressed were completely alien. Anyway, Thor would never willingly bring a woman to Danes' Dyke——'

At that instant the same thought struck them both.

'Britt!' Raine breathed.

'Father!' Vulcan hissed, his small frame tense with suppressed excitement. Seconds later he was off, chasing after the pair whose voices could still be heard murmuring in the distance.

She hesitated; the apprehension she had felt earlier was still with her stronger, indeed, than before. Britt, if it were he, seemed related to her mind to trouble, discord, upheaval, the disruption of a life which, lonely though it might be, was safe, secure and danger-free. The pair had sounded aggressively sophisticated; fiercely she resented their intrusion into her haven of seclusion!

She, too, began to run, but in the opposite direction, back towards the stables wherein she might find some measure of protection. So intent was she upon reaching them she failed to notice the Range Rover swinging off the moorland road. Her first intimation of danger was an agonized squeal of brakes and a salty curse that reached to where she

57

was trembling within inches of the powerful bonnet.

'What the blazes...! Are you intent upon getting yourself killed?' Her terror-filled look reminded Thor of the night she had fought against his supporting arms as if she had thought him a prospective murderer and his impatience faded as quickly as the colour from her cheeks. 'I'm sorry, it was probably my fault, I have a habit of driving too fast, specially on my own territory.'

'You have visitors,' she choked, a man and a woman. Vulcan seems to think the man might be his father!'

'*Britt!*' The name was hissed from between lips drawn narrow and she shivered, sensing the eruption of an anger forced by time and separation to smoulder low. 'Come with me!' When she tried to resist he grabbed her by the hand and began moving with giant strides towards the house, so keen to reach his goal he was heedless of her discomfiture as, forced to run, she took three steps to his one. She was breathless when they reached the house, content to remain panting against the door jamb while he released her to fling open the drawing-room door.

Two startled faces swivelled towards him when he halted, filling the doorway with his bulk, his expression vengeful as a Viking god. 'So you've finally come!' he grated, his eyes upon a tall, red-haired stranger comfortably installed in the depths of an armchair.

Raine watched, fascinated by the elegance with which the stranger rose to his feet, searching for signs of resemblance between the brothers. Physically they were well matched, the same height, same breadth of shoulder, same slimness of hip. But compared with Thor's baggy tweed jacket and corduroy slacks, Britt's suit was a masterpiece of sartorial perfection, jacket smoothly fitting, trousers creased knife sharp, and shoes of hand-tooled leather fitted snugly around ankles displaying discreetly patterned socks of pure silk. His hair was red — not rumped like his son's, nor wind-tossed like Thor's, but cleverly cut to give a casually well groomed look to his proudly tilted head.

Raine drew in a deep, shaken breath wondering, as her glance flew back to Thor, why he had adopted to hide similar good looks behind a masking beard.

Britt grinned at his glowering brother. 'As you can see,' he agreed lightly, 'the prodigal has returned.'

'Why?' Thor demanded bluntly.

'Why?' Britt repeated. 'Do I have to give a reason for returning home?'

At that moment Thor noticed Britt's companion, a blonde, fashionably dressed girl draped across the settee, smiling complacently.

'Good lord! Janice!' He sounded shaken. 'I thought you two were divorced!'

'Never actually got around to it, old son,' Britt breezed. 'After Father died, I knocked around the world a bit, then when insolvency became a problem I managed to convince a rich acquaintance of mine that I was both qualified and capable of skippering his precious yacht. A few months after he took me on he went broke—self-made millionaires usually do, I've found—but with the references he gave me I had no difficulty in finding other similar positions until finally I landed myself a job as skipper of one of the largest, most exclusive private yachts in existence. It's in dry dock at present, awaiting minor repairs, so you can look forward to the pleasure of our company for at least a month.'

Slowly, accusingly, Thor advanced further into the room. 'Are you daring to admit that for the past five years you've wasted your skill and expertise on a succession of toy ships? That instead of captaining your own, you've pandered to the whims of wealthy owners whose knowledge of seamanship is such they wouldn't know the difference between a skipper and a ship's cook?' Gritting his teeth with fury, he stressed, 'During the five years you've been away I've remained shorebound, unresentfully so, because all the while I've cherished an ideal of you making efforts to further your career so that one of us, at least, might follow the proud traditions of our family. You *owed* me that much,' he condemned bitterly, 'yet, typically, you've let me down!'

'I say, don't you think you're pushing this tradition thing a bit too far?' Britt protested, taking a way step backward. 'Besides,' he placated when Thor's eyes flashed, 'if I hadn't gone in for skippering yachts I might never have met up with Janice again. As it was, we bumped into each other in Monte, discovered the old magic was still going for us, and decided we wanted nothing more than to live together as a family, which is the real reason

60

we're here—to collect our son.'

'Over my dead body! was Thor's succinct, coldly determined reply.

Into the breach of silence a small bundle of fury erupted from behind the sofa. Vulcan, having adopted his usual eavesdropping tactics, had decided that this was the moment for him to have his say. 'I won't go with you, I *won't*!' he flung towards the strangers who had walked into his life. 'I'm staying here with Thor, he's my real daddy and ... and ...' Desperate for additional weight with which to balance his argument, his glance fell upon Raine's pale, bewildered face. 'And Raine is my mummy!' he lied triumphantly, 'So go away and leave us alone, we were happy together till you came!'

When every eye swung in her direction Raine wished fervently that she had the gift of making herself invisible. Awkwardly, she shuffled her feet, then blushing fiercely she sought for and found the strength of Thor's assurance. A plea for help seemed to project from eyes unusually desperate as he held her glance, willing her to understand his need. She answered him with a puzzled smile, then froze with astonishment when she heard him say,

'Britt, Janice, you haven't met my wife, Raine— as you can see Vulcan is devoted to her and she to him. Can you imagine any court in the land allowing you custody of a child you deserted five years ago, especially now when he's settled down to family life with a couple who love him and whom he regards as his parents? You could try, of course,' he challenged, 'but the ensuing publicity could be most unpleasant, perhaps unpleasant enough to make your rich boss think twice about employing a man so lacking in responsibility that for five years he didn't care a damn about the well-being of his son!'

Britt stared speechlessly at Thor, but Janice had eyes only for the stolid little figure who, for all his brave words, was struggling hard to suppress tears. She reached out to touch him and when he backed away she chided softly, '*I'm* your real mummy, darling, come, kiss me, we must get to know one another.'

Vulcan's mutinous bottom lip was very pronounced. 'Kissing is cissy, and you can't be my mummy, I've never seen you before!'

Raine felt a stab of pity for Janice, struggling to cope with a rush of maternal instincts and finding the experience strange. She winced when, instead of treading a careful path towards her son's affections, she chose to adopt stern, parental measures. 'Do as I say, Vulcan, come here this minute!'

He hesitated, teetering on the brink of obedience to the forceful command, then, casting a look of despair across the room, he found Raine and with a sob of thankfulness ran to her and was enfolded into her arms. She hugged him tightly, understanding and sharing his churning emotions. She, too, was bewildered by the suddenness with which she had been pitchforked into the centre of a family feud, promoted from the menial position of interloper to the dizzy heights of mistress of Danes' Dyke! Thor's motive was obvious—anxiety on Vulcan's behalf had driven him to employ desperate measures, but for the life of her she could not seen his plan succeeding. Janice and Britt were far from being fools and if, as had been stated, they intended remaining for at least a month they would easily ferret out the truth.

'You have your answer.' Thor sounded grimly satisfied. 'Even for a pair as egotistical as you two, the boy's action should be conviction enough that you've left it too late to play the role of parents—five years too late,' he stressed conclusively.

Janice swung a look of malice towards Raine, examining for the first time the girl by whom she had been usurped. A glint came into her eyes as slowly she examined the immature figure dressed in clothes so disreputable that the thought of feeling such coarse, utility garments against her own soft skin made her shudder. Sensing her projected contempt, Raine ran nervous fingers through her hair, then realized when Janice smiled that her action had betrayed a diffidence that would be exploited to the full by the woman she sensed was now her enemy.

'I refuse to accept such an answer!' There was bluster in Britt's tone and not a little pique. His conceit was such that he could not bear rejection in any form—especially not from the son he had reluctantly been forced into claiming. Winning Vulcan's love had now taken on a vital importance. 'Naturally, Thor, the boy has become attached to you and your ... wife.' Raine went hot as Britt's glance flickered over her. 'But trite though it may sound, blood is thicker than water and I intend to prove during the coming weeks that however much loyalty the boy feels he owes you, nothing can override the strength of ties between a child and his natural parents.'

Looking unnaturally tired, Thor replied, 'Unfortunately, I can't turn you out when—as I've no doubt you intended reminding me—Father willed that everything he owned was to be divided equally. You have as much right as I to live in this house——'

'And I have as much say in the running of it as your wife!' Janice intruded coldly. 'So to begin with, Raine, we'll have a fire lit in this gloomy hole, and would you please tell Simeon to prepare us a meal—we haven't eaten since breakfast and I'm starving!'

'Tell him yourself,' Thor directed, made furious by Janice's arrogant manner. 'While you're here you must be responsible for your own comfort. Raine has enough to do looking after Vulcan and myself. Also, be wary of upsetting Simeon,' he warned. 'He'll be put out enough when he learns there are now two masters and two mistresses at Danes' Dyke.'

To Raine's relief Thor then ushered herself and Vulcan out of the room, banging the door shut on their adversaries. 'Run outside and play,' he instructed Vulcan, ruffling the boy's hair with an encouraging hand. 'I want to talk to Raine.'

Without argument Vulcan obeyed, his dragging footsteps underlining his despondency. 'How I wish he could have been spared this upset!' Raine fretted, sharing the boy's torment.

'So do I,' Thor replied tersely, guiding her in the

direction of his den, 'but if our plan works it may be the last hurt they'll ever inflict upon him.'

Our plan! Even though the situation was grave she could not help the glow she felt at being included in the conspiracy.

'But how *can* it work?' She spun to face him as he closed the door. 'There are too many people who know we're not married, and what's more, know we've never even considered the possibility.'

She knew he was worried when he fumbled for a cigarette rather than the pipe with the thumb-smoothed bowl which was rarely out of his reach. She waited, and after drawing so deeply the tip glowed an angry red, he muttered a stiff apology. 'I'm sorry to have dragged you into this mess, I don't usually act on impulse, but in this instance the words were out before the intention was actually formed. It seemed a good ruse to get rid of them in a hurry. After all, what I said was true—those two would have the devil of a job proving they had more right to the boy than we who have reared him from birth. I know it and they know it, but unfortunately they seem determined to bide their time, and if ever they discover we're not married ... ! Dammit!' he clamped, 'I ought to have considered the harm this situation would do to your reputation. Janice will have a field day if ever she finds out!'

'Then for Vulcan's sake we'll have to make sure she doesn't!' she declared, hooking her thumbs into her belt with such a show of gentle belligerence that Thor's mouth twitched. Ignoring his amusement, she laboured on, 'Whom can we trust?'

Her composure took a battering when he strode across to seize her by the shoulders. 'There's no reason on earth why you shouldn't walk out of here this minute and declare me a liar!' he clipped. 'Be quite certain you know exactly what you're doing before becoming involved further.'

Through her jumper his fingers scorched her skin and for a moment a thousand butterfly wings beat wildly in her throat, rendering her incapable of an answer. But finally she gasped, 'I'll do anything to help Vulcan!' As he stared silently down at her she found herself wishing she could penetrate the screening beard. Why did he cherish it so, she wondered—was it in order to hide any fleeting tenderness that might otherwise be reflected in his face?

'Are you quite sure?' When she nodded he released her and stepped away. 'Then first of all we must take Simeon into our confidence—that's essential,' he assured her when she gasped a protest.

Reluctantly she nodded, resigning herself to suffering yet more resentment from the old man who had already declared his suspicions in that direction.

'With Simeon on our side we needn't worry about the rest of the men, he'll put them in the picture only when and if he thinks it necessary, which shouldn't be ever,' he frowned. 'Britt hates the land and everything connected with it, so he's hardly likely to venture outside except when entering or leaving his car. No, Janice is the one we must watch,' he pondered gravely, 'she'll pry into every corner of the house, asking awkward questions, probing as far as she dare up to the limit of impertinence.' Deliberately, he stressed, 'Luckily, our rooms are adjoining, the key to the connecting door has long been lost, but it shouldn't be too difficult to pick the lock. Will you mind your loss of privacy? Naturally, I shan't venture across the threshold unless circumstances make it imperative, but if our plan is to succeed it must be authentic.'

'Do whatever you feel you must,' she gasped, feeling suddenly stripped.

'Thank you. Then our only other worry is Vulcan. Lord only knows what he might let slip, but I've no intention of tutoring him to lies. The little devil instigated this scheme by electing you his mother, and I'm hoping natural cunning will guide him along the lines of discretion. Anyway, on that score, we can but trust to luck.'

Just when she had been regaining a little of her lost composure, she was disconcerted to find him once more looming over her. 'Try not to worry,' he encouraged in a tone so gentle it turned her heart over. 'My brother and his wife are a selfish, luxury-loving pair who'll soon tire of life on the moors. I can almost guarantee that in less than a month we'll be free of them and left to resume life on the same lines as before.'

CHAPTER SIX

JANICE was horrified when informed by Thor that if she and Britt were staying they would have to prepare a room for themselves.

'Why should we?' she gasped, her doll-like features set in a mask of outrage.

'Because I have no intention of employing extra household staff and Simeon already has enough to do in the kitchen. The only two bedrooms habitable are occupied by Raine and myself.'

Britt and Janice had just finished a meal, of sorts, dished up by a very disgruntled Simeon who had made plain his objection to being ordered about by Janice, whose demands had been unsweetened by tact.

'You mean you have a bedroom each?' Her calculating look made Raine squirm. 'In that case, surely you can spare us one—after all, it will only be for a few weeks?'

'Out of the question.' Thor refused blandly. 'I'm a very early riser; I see no reason why Raine should suffer loss of sleep when there are plenty of other bedrooms available.' The clash of personalities was almost audible in the room dominated by Thor's tall figure. Coldly, Janice eyed him, her lip curling as she compared with with her husband who, even though lounging in an armchair, was still managing to retain his air of elegance. Unruffled, Thor weathered the unspoken criticism and with a coolness Raine envied continued to direct, 'I'm sure Raine won't mind finding you dusters and whatever else you might need, and no doubt Britt will give you a hand with the heavier chores.'

With sweet acidity, Janice veered from the subject. 'How long did you say you two have been married?' Her eyes were on Thor, but she did not miss Raine's startled jerk.

'I didn't,' Thor calmly continued stuffing tobacco into his pipe. 'The question never arose.'

Britt stirred, lazily interested. 'It has arisen now. Tell me,' he addressed Raine, 'how long have I been in possession of such a delightful sister-in-law?'

Her blush owed nothing to the tongue-in-cheek compliment, but was born of confusion and stampeding panic. 'I . . . we . . .' she stammered, searching wildly for inspiration.

'The ceremony took place just a few weeks ago,' Thor supplied unblinkingly, 'but for personal reasons we've kept our marriage a secret and would prefer it to remain that way until Raine's family has been informed.'

'Really . . . ?' Janice gave them a long, curious look. 'How romantic, don't you think so, Britt darling? Who would believe that this sobersided brother of yours was capable of sweeping a girl so swiftly off her feet that she married him without waiting even for her parents' blessing? Do they live nearby?' Her keen, probing eyes swung to Raine, determined to ferret out the maximum of information.

Raine's brow wrinkled as, for a split second, a memory flitted tantalizingly close. 'They don't live . . . in England,' she supplied haltingly, conscious of Thor's intent stare.

'Then where?' Janice prompted. 'Or is that information also classified?'

Britt surprised them all with an easy assurance. 'In Ireland, I bet! That trace of brogue in Raine's voice has been puzzling me for hours, but at last I've placed its origin. I'm right, Raine, am I not?'

White-faced, she searched for Thor and found encouragement in his smile. He moved to her side and she felt immeasurably protected when his arm slid around her waist. 'I suppose we shall have to tell them,' be bluffed, tightening his grip on her slender, wilting frame. 'Raine's parents are on holiday in Canada,' he lied without a blush. 'As she didn't want to join them she decided during their absence to do a bit of touring on her own. Luckily for me, Yorkshire took her fancy; she was lost on the moors and I found her. A few weeks later I proposed, but as her parents aren't due back home for three months we prefer to keep our marriage a secret until they've been told.'

Everyone was rendered speechless by this admission, but finally Janice surfaced. 'How very unusual,' she breathed, eyeing Raine as if she were a specimen of some unclassified being, 'so you actually know very little about her, she could be anyone—a criminal even—yet you expect me to leave her in charge of my son!'

'Oh, come now . . . !' Even Britt was embarrassed by his wife's lack of delicacy.

'I assure you Raine is no criminal,' Thor leapt to her defence, 'on the contrary, she's too basically gentle, she should never have been allowed to roam a strange county alone.'

'I don't agree!' Janice retorted with more than a touch of malice. 'It seems to me she's already proved herself capable of the impossible by reversing the opinions of a woman-hating recluse!'

After Janice, closely followed by Britt, had swept out of the room Raine began wondering if her last parting shot was responsible for the awkwardness Thor was displaying. For a huge man his movements were surprisingly agile, yet twice he bumped into furniture in a hasty bid to move out of her path and he flushed a dull red whenever her gently enquiring look turned his way. It was a relief when he decided to relieve her of his company.

'I have some work to do in my study,' he muttered, 'don't bother about dinner for me, I'll beg a sandwich from Simeon later.'

Left to herself, Raine stared thoughtfully out of the window. According to Britt, she was Irish. His remark about her accent had struck a familiar chord and she was glad of the chance to concentrate in solitude, to try to solidify transient memories knocking on the door of her mind. Was he right, and if she were Irish would that help to explain her shocked state on the night Thor had found her? Only the other day she had picked up one of the few newspapers that found their way into the house and had read with horror details of the bomb outrages and murders being committed in the land torn apart by the Troubles. Had she been involved, had she perhaps flown from the sight of some massacre, boarded a ship—any ship—then after finding herself on the west coast of England had she continued fleeing eastward so as to put as much distance as possible between herself and the cause of her distress? Her head was aching by the time she decided there was nothing to be gained from further agonizing. Wearily, she slid from the windowseat to go in search of Vulcan, whose suppertime was imminent, having finally accepted the futility of trying to force a way through the barriers erected around her mind.

She found him in the kitchen talking to Simeon and was amazed when, instead of the usual surly reception the old man greeted her with a conspiratorial grin. 'Evening, miss,' he confounded her further. 'The boy's had his supper, he's just finishing off his milk.'

'So I see,' she returned shyly, 'but you already have far too much to do, Simeon, you simply must allow me to help.'

For a while he fought with his conscience. Obviously Thor had put him in the picture and he approved of the ruse being perpetrated for the sake of the boy, but to accept a woman in his kitchen was asking a lot and truculence was present in his tone when he finally answered. 'Master Britt's wife has *instructed* that in future dinner is to be served in the dining-room each evening. No doubt she'll be expecting lace mats, best china and polished silver!' He gave a short, bitter laugh. 'I fear she's going to be disappointed!'

'Let me arrange the table,' she offered eagerly,

'then you'll be free to concentrate on preparing the meal. I'd like to, Simeon, really I would, not just to help out but to show her——' She stopped abruptly; however keenly she felt Janice's contempt it was not fair to try to enlist the sympathy of the servants.

Simeon, however, was way ahead of her. His head shot up as with a gleam of triumph he urged, 'Do that, Miss Raine, surprise her by laying a table fit for a queen and I promise she'll have no cause to complain about the meal. Moors folk we may be, but ignorant we are not, and between us we'll prove it!'

On a wave of enthusiasm they began their preparations. Once having seen a very reluctant Vulcan off to bed, Raine began searching through linen chests to unearth carefully preserved napery smelling delightfully of lavender; gathered together for washing selected items from a huge, dusty dinner service, then settled in a corner of the kitchen to the task of removing years of tarnish from cutlery of finely engraved silver. At first they worked in silence, Simeon's gnarled fingers plying a kitchen knife with surprising speed through a succession of vegetables before turning his skill and attention to the preparing of various courses.

Greatly daring, she ventured, 'Have you decided what the menu is to be?' Then when his brow beetled, suspecting interference, she rushed on, 'I need to know how many places to set ... for how many courses ...' she faded miserably.

His rugged smile revived her spirits. 'I thought of lobster cocktail as a starter,' he informed her kindly, 'then minestrone soup. Sautéed kidneys should go down well as an entrée and, as Master Thor is very partial to a nice piece of steak, I'm doing T-bone with veg for the main course, then to follow, pineapple sloshed over with some of that Kirsch liqueur that's been standing in the drinks cabinet for ages, with a selection of cheeses for them as wants 'em,' he finished with a flourish, gratified by her wide-eyed admiration.

'Perfect!' she congratulated him, wondering if she dared offer to help with the preparing of the more difficult dishes. She decided against it, however, being too cowardly to risk arousing the wrath of the old man whose new, favourable attitude had come about merely as a result of having had to give allegiance to one of two mistresses—his choice being governed by the maxim: better the devil you know than the devil you don't!'

For a while longer they continued working in silence, then once again she decided to chance her luck. 'Did ... has Captain Halden explained the situation that's arisen?' she asked, fire burning her cheeks.

'About you two being secretly wed? Yes,' he concluded abruptly.

She waited for a follow-up, but none came. 'You must have been surprised,' she soldiered on, 'but Captain Halden insists there's no other way.'

'A man of sound judgement, the Skipper,' Simeon pronounced flatly. 'If he says there's no other way then there *is* no other way.'

'You're very fond of him, aren't you?' she challenged softly. 'But then you must be equally fond

74

of his brother, too, having known them both from childhood?'

'Fond of Britt!' he snorted with startling vehemence. 'The Skipper won't have it said, but that brother of his is no more than a playboy, any man who's ever served under him will vouch for that. Brilliant he may be in some respects, but any sailor given a choice would prefer to sail the Arctic under the Skipper's command than cruise in a warmer hemisphere with his brother! Only women are fooled by false smiles and pretty manners—men go for a man they can trust!'

After his stormy outburst, Raine decided it would be politic to clear out of the kitchen, so hastily she began transferring everything she needed into the dining-room to set about a display which she hoped would do justice to the promised excellence of the meal. Before leaving the kitchen for the last time she hesitated. 'What about wine? They're sure to expect ...'

'Master Thor will attend to that.'

'Oh, but he said not to bother him with dinner!' she suddenly remembered, her sense of excitement quickly deflating.

'He'll change his mind once he knows the score,' Simeon stated with a confidence Raine, however much she tried, could not bring herself to share.

It was seven-thirty by the time she was satisfied that the dinner table was looking as attractive as she could make it. She stood back to admire her handiwork, pleased with the sheen of silver reflecting from a polished surface scattered with delicately crocheted mats, slender crystal goblets and fine plate splashed with a pattern of vivid full-blown poppies. The centrepiece, a shallow silver bowl she had found pushed to the back of a cupboard, was filled with poppies picked half an hour earlier, and its glorious spill of colour was evocative of a kiss—petal-smooth lips quivering and pouting.

She sighed, reminded for some reason of Thor's previous unease. It was as if Janice's spiteful remark had given rise to the suspicion that she might read more than was intended into his enforced friendliness, and he had therefore decided to retreat once more into the shell he had so fleetingly abandoned. Which was a pity, she reflected with a blush, because the short interval of truce had been so enjoyable that not even the seriousness of the events leading up to it had dimmed the pleasure she had felt in his approval!

It was not until she went up to her room that a dreadful thought struck her. She had nothing to wear! Each evening, after seeing Vulcan to bed, she had formed the habit of slipping into a cumbersome, masculine dressing-gown she had found abandoned in the huge wardrobe so as to wash through the only items of underwear she possessed. The flimsy, drip-dry garments were then hung up to dry, ready for wearing the following morning, and though at first she had shuddered from such repetitive use, pride had forced her to accept the situation rather than approach Thor with a request for money. Obviously, she could not dine in the company of Janice and Britt clothed in shrunken jeans and a misshapen sweater, so the only alternative was to send an excuse for absence and remain

76

in her room until such time as she judged it safe to slip down to the kitchen and forage.

The sound of knuckles rapping on the connecting door made her jump. Nervously she called out permission to enter and, marooned on a sea of carpet, she tensed, awaiting Thor's unprecedented appearance in her bedroom. He strode in, hiding his embarrassment behind cool abruptness.

'Aren't you ready yet!' His eyebrows met above a straight blade of nose. 'According to Simeon the success or failure of this dinner depends entirely upon how we conduct ourselves this evening, so a late start will hardly be conducive to good humour. The appropriate wines have been decanted, and as you can see, I've been bullied into dressing up and presenting myself as an escort. Will I pass muster?'

Disappointment almost choked her as she cast an eye over the tall figure, unfamiliar in a dark suit, pristine shirt and a tie flaunting an emblem decidedly nautical. 'You look very nice,' she commented feebly. Struggling to appear unconcerned, she sauntered as casually as she was able across to the window. 'Do you mind if I don't join you downstairs? I'm not very hungry and also I have rather a bad headache.'

When he reached her in two enormous strides it was too late to wish she had chosen a dark corner in which to make her stand. Late evening sun was flooding through the window, highlighting cheeks flushed with health and eyes a vital, startling blue.

'Liar!' The whispered indictment could not have shocked more had it been shouted. 'Now tell me the real reason—fear of Janice, or just a natural desire to avoid the pitfalls of deceit?'

'Neither, I promise you,' she assured him hastily, soothed by his obvious regret. 'It's simply—*well, just look at me!*' she burst out, goaded by his masculine blindness to a woman's needs.

For a puzzled second he stared down at her slight defiant figure. Then: 'Good lord!' he said simply, 'I *am* an unthinking fool!'

His realization hurt more than his blindness. Before, her appearance had barely registered, but now he was seeing her as she really was, shabby, unkempt and decidedly unglamorous. She spun from his sight when tears spurted, furtively mopping up her humiliation on a baggy sleeve, and felt mortified by his quietly voiced assurance, 'Don't fret, I'll think of some excuse that won't arouse suspicion. Janice and Britt must not guess the reason behind your non-appearance at dinner.'

Raine remained with her back turned until she was sure he had left the room, then in an orgy of self-pity she flung herself upon the bed to wallow in a flood of tears, muttering fierce condemnations between sobs. 'Won't guess! I bet they will! Not everyone is so blindly obtuse he can't see when clothes are falling off a person's back! It didn't matter before—there was no one with whom I could be compared, but now ...! Oh, *damnation!*' she burrowed her face deep into the soaking pillow, 'I wish I were *dead!*'

Much later she stirred and gazed dazedly around the bedroom. Judging from the shadows filling each corner she must have been asleep for hours. She slid from the bed, reminded of her evening chore, and had just begun washing when she heard a low, urgent tapping on the connecting door. She stiffened and held her breath, willing him to go away, but when the tapping was resumed, impatiently louder, she had no choice but to open the door.

'What do you want?' she hissed through an aperture narrow enough to conceal her small figure engulfed by the comically-large dressing-gown.

'I've brought you some food,' he whispered back, sensitive of eavesdroppers. 'I waited until Janice and Britt had gone to bed, then slipped into the kitchen to fill a tray. You must be famished,' his purposeful foot prised the aperture wider. 'Here, catch hold of this while I fetch the wine.'

The tray was thrust into her hands and too startled to protest, she remained still, afraid to move in case she should trip over the yards of hem flowing around her feet. He returned in seconds, carrying a slim-necked bottle and two glasses, and at the sight of her incongruously clad figure his lips twitched, though his voice was roughly grave when he apologized, 'I'm sorry, I didn't realize your predicament—let me take the tray while you find yourself a seat.'

Putting on as dignified a front as possible, she handed back the tray, then, gathering up as much as she could handle of the surplus material, she tottered across to the bed and sat down, tucking her feet beneath her.

'Are you hungry?' he queried, settting the tray down beside her.

'Terribly,' she confessed. 'It was agony lying here

79

knowing Simeon was serving dishes specially concocted to impress Janice. 'Was she impressed?' she asked eagerly, sinking small white teeth into a large piece of utterly delicious cold steak.

'Amazed would be a more apt description,' he smiled. 'We all of us were, Simeon included. You must have dedicated hours of your time to the perfectly appointed table; I must admit I've never realized before this evening how devoid Danes' Dyke has been of a woman's touch. You have the gift of turning a house into a home,' he conceded slowly. 'I appreciate your allowing us to benefit from that gift.'

Raine stared, arrested between bites, her hunger forgotten as she digested his words. It hardly seemed credible that his brusque, no-nonsense manner could have been hiding a yearning for the light feminine touches both he and his father had banned for ever from their lives. Yet was it so incredible? After all, she had not already experienced the touch of velvet beneath the iron glove of Thor, recovered unscathed from his vocal hammer blows, and felt grateful for the security of his constricting belt . . . ?

Carefully she laid down the remaining morsel of meat and dared to search the face made so aggravatingly inscrutable by the blazing red beard. Green eyes met blue in a steady gaze that stripped her of bravery, left her breathless, unsure and full of awkward shyness. She wished now that she had concentrated upon the food he had provided, accepted without question his kindly action instead of probing for wildly improbable motives.

'Have some wine.' At the clink of bottle against glass she winced, enduring the pain of a broken spell.

'Th-thank you,' she stuttered, and reached for the proffered glass with a hand obscured by a dangling cuff. Hastily she rolled it back, discomfited by his grin, then felt needles of fire when their fingers touched around the crystal stem. Simultaneously they snatched their hands away and the abandoned glass spilled a stain of red wine on to the bedcover.

'Oh, the mess!' she cried, near to tears.

'What a fuss you women do make over trifles!' he clipped, moving impatiently away. 'It will soon dry, for heaven's sake!'

She longed to explain away her nervousness, but dared not risk upsetting further the equilibrium of a man already torn apart by, on the one hand, gratitude for her help, and on the other, resentment of her disruption of his masculine stronghold. So she concentrated on mopping up the slowly-spreading stain while he strode towards the door, and lifted a pale, unhappy face to his when he hesitated just long enough to command,

'What I really came for was to tell you that to-morrow I'm going into York on business, so you might as well come with me. As I want to make an early start I've told Simeon to serve breakfast early. Seven o'clock sharp!' he ordered. 'Don't keep me waiting!'

CHAPTER SEVEN

THOR had finished breakfast when she arrived downstairs the following morning, but as it was just after six-thirty he sent an approving look across the top of his newspaper when she slid into a chair and began helping herself from dishes containing kidneys and bacon. As he continued reading she peeped at the back page and finding it contained nothing more exciting than farming news, weeks out of date, she decided his interest could hardly be urgent and nerved herself to speak.

'Shall I waken Vulcan now?—it will take at least half an hour to get him ready.'

The paper rustled as it was lowered to the table. 'Vulcan isn't coming,' he surprised her by saying, 'he can be left in the care of his parents for one day.'

'He won't like that, he's sure to misbehave.'

'I'm counting on that!' His sudden grin almost stopped her heart. 'The devil himself is good when he's pleased—it's time Janice and Britt discovered for themselves that their offspring, when crossed, can be far from angelic.'

Still confused by the warmth of his smile, she countered on a breath, 'So that's why we're disappearing for the day! Very clever!'

'Devious,' he contradicted wryly, 'but there's another reason behind our proposed outing. No,' he shook his head when she began interrupting. 'I've no intention of divulging further, when you're ready we'll be on our way.'

It was a beautiful morning. As they drove along the deserted moorland road the air felt soft against her cheeks, full of warm promise, and high into a cloudless sky a lark soared, light as her heart, its trill of pleasure an echo of her own rising excitement. Thor glanced down at her while he drove, his lips quirking as he recognized childish anticipation on her expressive face. 'Pixie face,' he murmured, then at her surprised look he continued on a different tack. 'The thought of visiting town obviously pleases you.' He sighed with mock resignation. 'I suppose I'm to be subjected to the wearisome chore of escorting you around the shops—an exercise in which females seem to delight?'

Blue eyes widened with surprise. 'Oh, no ... I wouldn't dream of expecting ... anyway, you have business to attend to, you said so.'

His enigmatic smile was as intriguing as his laconic response. 'Why must it always be assumed that business can be conducted only in official places?'

Raine could think of no answer to that, so, sensing he would refuse to elaborate further, she abandoned the subject to confess, 'I *am* rather looking forward to doing a bit of window shopping, to studying the latest fashions. I'm not a bad dressmaker really, once I managed to copy an evening dress so exactly——' She stopped, conscious of his sudden interest, and the vague memory vanished. Desolation swamped her, all the bubbling excitement she had been feeling, the happiness, the sheer joy of living, fled before the reminder of his doubt about her loss of memory. It would be useless trying to explain to a disbeliever how these tantalizing remnants of her past could float within reach, then disappear the moment they came within grasp.

Her dejection went so deep she was not aware that he had run off the road until he applied the brake, halting the car with a savage jerk. Even then she did not bother to look up, but waited with downcast eyes for the expected catechism.

'You mustn't concern yourself so much.' The pity in his voice was unbelievable. 'I'm sorry I haven't been of much help—my stupid blindness to the state of your clothes, for instance—but——'

'Sorry? Why should you be sorry to see me dressed like the tramp you've always insisted I am?' Dignity lifted her chin and added sparkle to eyes previously dulled.

Conscience caused him to flush. 'I was wrong.' The admission, almost strangled by pride, had difficulty forcing a way past his lips. Thor the master, the self-sufficient, the law unto himself, was not used to unbending, especially not to a woman.

'Over the past weeks I've realized more and more the impossibility of your ever filling such a role,' he grated, resentful of having to woo her forgiveness yet grimly set to stay the course. 'In a thousand ways you've impressed upon all of us your inherent good breeding, and though you're no fashion plate,' he opined bluntly, 'you possess an elegance that enables one to overlook the fact that you're clothed in rags.'

She winced, but quickly reviving spirits tugged

her drooping mouth upwards. On a deeply in-drawn breath she demanded, 'Are you saying you now believe me?'

'Without reservation,' he amazed her by answering, 'I don't believe you would ever willingly lie.'

As they neared civilization, passing occasional cars, a sprinkling of farms, then a gradual build up of houses, her boyish frame felt barely able to contain a swell of happiness. When traffic became thicker Thor had to concentrate on his driving, so nothing further was said until they reached the outskirts of York where, as they approached, Raine was riveted by the sight of mellow stone fashioning the walls and archways of the ancient fortress city.

'How wonderful!' she gasped, and was lost for further words as they entered narrow streets where tiny shops, their ancient roofs dipping and swaying, jostled shoulder to shoulder, their medieval front-ages vying to catch the interest of passers-by. It took little imagination to picture the cobbled streets ringing to the sound of horses' hooves as carriages deposited crinolined ladies on the very doorsteps of genteel establishments; to drapers eager to display huge bolts of cloth; to candymakers where they could dither over red lips, coconut kisses, humbugs or heart-shaped cachous chosen either for the apt-ness of their printed mottoes or as a means of acquiring a sweetly-scented breath; or to a mil-liners to have designed a poke bonnet strewn with ribbons and rosebuds.

She abandoned her fantasies when the central tower of the Minster rose up in front of them, a church of honey-coloured stone built hundreds of years before on the site of a Roman legionary fortress, Thor told her, his words barely penetrating her rapt enjoyment of the magnificent stone edifice sculpted with dragons' heads, gargoyles, pious saints with hands clasped in prayer and windows of coloured glass with heart-shaped tracery showing a knight and his lady come on pilgrimage to St. Peter, the Minster's patron saint.

Realization that the car had drawn to a standstill came as a shock, and for confused seconds she had to fight her way out of the past in order to make sense of Thor's words.

'Do you intend sitting there all day?' he asked pleasantly.

She scrambled from the car, hopping from one foot to the other while he made sure each door was secure, and felt immense disappointment when, instead of offering to show her around the Minster, he led her firmly in the opposite direction, ignoring the longing glances she kept casting over her shoulders.

'Can't we take just one peep inside?' she begged, dragging her feet.

'Later,' he promised. 'First of all we must attend to a matter of some urgency.'

Raine trotted to keep up with his giant strides, wondering as she did so why he should consider her presence necessary to the success of his business, and was more than ever puzzled when he stopped outside of a large department store set in the middle of a shopping precinct. 'This ought to do,' he grunted, edging her through plate glass doors then into a lift that whisked them upwards, disgorging them finally into an over-heated, thickly carpeted department lined with racks of coats, suits and dresses.

'A dress for this young woman,' he instructed an approaching saleslady, hiding his embarrassment under a crust of ill humour. The woman stared at the red-bearded giant clutching the hand of a shrinking figure which at first sight she had taken to be a boy. But when, upon more detailed examination, she glimpsed an eye-catching line of thigh, a suggestion of curves and the promise of a slender waist buried beneath the voluminous sweater she smiled encouragement towards the frightened child. The morning which had began as boringly as any other now seemed to teem with promise. Briskly she escorted them to an isolated corner and after flourishing a curtain across the vision of giggling juniors, waved Thor towards a chair and concentrated her attention upon Raine.

'What sort of dress does Madame require—cocktail, evening or day wear?'

'One of each,' Thor instructed, perching uneasily astride a spindle-legged chair.

When the assistant drifted away, Raine rounded furiously to hiss, 'I don't want you to buy me clothes, I'll wait until I have some money of my own!'

'When will that be?' he returned calmly. 'If our plan is to work you must dress respectably. Britt knows I'm not short of money and would be sure to suspect something was amiss if you continued going around dressed like a scarecrow. Besides,' the fragile chair creaked as he leant forward to stress, 'you've worked darned hard these past weeks without pay, so however much your outfit costs it can come out of your accumulated wages.'

She was given no chance to argue further. For the next hour a bewildering selection of outfits were paraded in front of her, most of them, it seemed to her shocked eyes, being given Thor's nod of approval. Even an evening dress presented by the enthusiastic saleslady, who by now was convinced she was involved in the choosing of a trousseau, was included among the clothes piled high on one side ready for removal to the car.

When finally he was satisfied they had purchased all she needed, he drew her out of earshot of the inquisitive saleslady and murmured, 'Do you think you can manage on your own for an hour or two? I'll come back for this lot,' he nodded towards the parcels, 'after I've seen to some business of my own.' Seeming in a desperate hurry to be on his way, he pushed a bundle of banknotes into her hand. 'There must be other fripperies you need,' he mumbled. 'I'll pick you up outside the main entrance in a couple of hours.' He was gone before she could protest, eating up the carpet with his rangy stride so that in no time at all his tall figure had disappeared from view and she was left clutching the bundle of notes, her heart overflowing with strange, new, inexplicable emotions.

Undecided, she bit her lip, hovering between a desire to push the money into her pocket in order to return it intact, and the necessity of acquiring fresh underwear—a need even more urgent now that she had piles of new clothes. Still tussling with her conscience, she made her way out of the department, descended a flight of stairs, passed tempting displays without a glance, then was abruptly halted by the absence of an exit out of the department into which she had wandered. She looked around and drew in an envious breath, her problem resolved. No girl could help but covet the rainbow display of frothing lace, silks and chiffons fashioned into slips, nightdresses and negligées so ethereal a puff of wind could have blown them away.

She reached out to caress with one finger a luxurious sweep of candy-pink nylon and at a touch was lost, overwhelmed by the temptation to feel once again the pleasant stroke of silk against her skin, to feel fresh, clean, *feminine*!

Within fifteen minutes, with the help of an obliging assistant, she had purchased all she needed, then flushed with excitement, she gathered up her parcels and made her way back to the dress department to add them to the waiting pile.

'Does Madame wish to wear one of the dresses now?' The question, accompanied by a sweeping glance over her dreadful sweater, was unmistakable in implication.

'Yes ... why not?' Raine stammered, the prospect of surprising Thor with a completely new image heightening the colour in her cheeks. 'Leave out the yellow one,' she decided, full of eager impatience to be clothed in a dress the colour of sunshine.

Her fingers trembled so much she could barely hook up a diaphanous brassiere and her limbs shivered their delight as a silken slip slid across her skin and settled sensuously around her curves. She could have purred with pleasure. Her heart was racing like a mad thing, her knees wilting, and when finally she pirouetted before a mirror wearing the yellow dress her face was that of a happy pixie, eyes brilliant, her expression full of joy.

'Might I offer a further suggestion?' The saleswoman felt blinded by the brilliance of Raine's smile. 'We have a hairdressing salon here in the store—if you like, I could make you an appointment.'

Raine's hand flew to her tangled mop of hair. 'You're very kind,' she faltered, 'it would be nice to have a hair-do, but my friend will be returning in just over an hour and I mustn't keep him waiting.'

'But there's every chance that the salon will fit you in immediately,' she was assured.

A short time later she was ensconced in a cubicle, squirming under the surveillance of a young man who, if his frown was indicative, did not think much of the challenge that had been thrown his way. As he smoothed a comb through her hair his frown darkened. 'Hmmm ... the condition of your hair is good, but the cutting ... !' She actually felt him shudder. 'I'll do the best I can, but whoever styled Madame's hair must have used a hatchet!'

She enjoyed the pampered luxury of a shampoo and set, but fidgeted under the drier, barely able to contain her eagerness to see the finished result. When the last roller had been removed the success of the young man's artistry was immediately evident. Carefully he smoothed his comb through a neat black cap that captured perfectly the elfin quality he had been quick to recognize, feathering strands across her brow and cheeks to give her the look of a cheeky urchin. He even unbent far enough to smile agreement when she gasped, 'How clever of you—my hair looks wonderful!'

She was teetering on her toes outside the main entrance of the store, enjoying the pinch of new shoes, when she saw Britt striding in her direction. She blushed self-consciously when his glance flickered over her, then felt humiliated when he passed her by without a word of acknowledgement. While she waited for Thor she kept sneaking looks at her image reflected in the plate glass windows, feeling mounting excitement at the knowledge that she was looking better than she had ever looked before. She swung round to scan the crowd and saw Britt retracing his steps, obviously on the look out for someone. She braced, then when he came within earshot she hailed him. 'Hello, Britt, I had no idea you intended coming to York. Is Vulcan with you?'

To her surprise he seemed disconcerted, his face registering the acute embarrassment of a person at a loss to place the identity of an acquaintance.

'I'm terribly sorry——' he began, then in that split second recognition was mutual.

'Thor—you've shaved off your beard!'

'Good lord!' was his blank, stunned reply.

'I thought you were Britt,' she rambled, weak in voice and at the knees. 'It wasn't until you spoke, your voice is so much deeper...'

'Like a clapped-out foghorn,' he agreed wryly, without interrupting his amazed assessment.

'Like a rich, resonant bell,' she dimpled, feeling suddenly shy of the handsome stranger who was eyeing her with such approval.

'You have very shapely legs.' He stepped back for a better view, his teasing twinkle adding to her confusion.

Raine fought for composure and breathed a laugh. 'Haven't you seen them before?' A flood of confusion overwhelming her as suddenly she re-called wakening in a strange bedroom stripped of her clothes and wearing an unfamiliar nightdress.

'Once,' he confirmed her worst suspicions, 'but in rather more clinical circumstances.'

He was enjoying her discomfiture, she realized, struggling unsuccessfully to equate the old Thor with the new. It was as if the barber and shaved away not only his beard but also the scowl that generally accompanied it, and with the disappear-ance of the two he looked years younger and dis-turbingly handsome.

He relented, taking pity on the elfin figure, so petite he felt a need to pick her up and put her in his pocket for safe keeping. Gruffly, because the thought amazed him, he reached for her hand and offered, 'I know you're dying to tour the city, where would you like to begin?'

Naturally, she chose the Minster. She would willingly have spent the whole of their allotted time within the awe-inspiring cathedral, revelling in an atmosphere soaked in history, reading aloud inscriptions chased upon stone couches supporting lifelike effigies of those entombed, or simply gaz-ing in silence upon the beauty wrought in glass and stone. But he allowed her only one hour to examine the interior before ushering her towards a spiral staircase cut from stone leading, he informed her, up to the roof.

The steps seemed never-ending, hundreds of them, fan-shaped, curling up and up, so narrow in width that at times Thor's broad shoulders were brushing the supporting walls. Laughingly, he encouraged her when three-quarters of the way up she called a halt, pleading exhaustion.

'Just one final effort,' he urged, propelling her forward with hands that descended firmly around her waist. His touch was electric. Volts of energy tingled along her spine and every nerve was alerted by a vibrancy that flowed upon contact, shocking in its urgency. Her faltering footsteps regained speed as she tried to outreach the hands that were burning an imprint on her skin, but he seemed determined to retain his hold and merely quickened his steps, proving with a chuckle the lack of strain involved in the effort.

The view when they finally reached the roof was well worth the strenuous assent. Alone in their eyrie, they looked down upon a toy town populated by pygmies, tiny cars and buses, threaded by rivers, landscaped with inch-square lawns and miniature oak trees. Wind whipped ruffling fingers through her hair, and as she reached up to protect it he captured her hands within his grasp.

'Leave it!' he commanded. 'I prefer it that way.'

She trembled when his fingers began combing gently through the sculptured cap, loosening tendrils that fluttered in a breeze as crazily erratic as her heart. She turned her head aside, pretending interest in the scene below, and felt cast adrift on powerful seas when his fingers grasped her chin, forcing her to meet his eyes. 'Fey creature,' she heard him murmur. 'Celtic witch!' He swooped, crushing her lips beneath his urgent mouth. It was a strange kiss, containing curiosity, an urge to experiment, and an indifference to response that was insulting. Raine fought hard against an instinct to surrender to the man she had come to love—so stealthily that the knowledge came as a shock. She would have given everything of herself had she felt loved, but his actions betrayed mere physical need, his methods barely short of plunder!

Feeling soiled by his touch, she tore out of his arms and employed her only means of defence—scorn—the one weapon guaranteed to scar a man of pride.

'Had I realized the kind of payment you would expect, I would have walked around in rags indefinitely rather than accept your charity!'

He whitened, and for a moment she felt sure he was about to strike her, yet she felt no fear—her feelings were too ravaged to allow further pain. Neither did she feel pity for the man whose chiselled features wore the outraged mask of one whose ego has been flicked raw. How *dared* he expect to find her willing to fulfil a passing whim!

Making a supreme effort, he weathered the insult, scorning even to deny the accusation flung so bitterly at his head.

'Shall we go?' When he indicated with a curt nod the circular swoop of stairs Raine stumbled towards them wishing, as she began the long trek down, that she had wings with which to flee the shadow casting fury over her dejected head.

The day that had begun with a jump for joy ended with a feeling that someone had moved the ground from beneath her feet. Not a word was exchanged between them during the furious drive back to Danes' Dyke. The sun still shone, the sky was just as blue, the birdsong as sweet, but within the confines of the car the atmosphere was explosive enough to be ignited by a single rash word.

Wisely, she left him to seethe, huddling as far away as possible from the red-haired giant whose rough overtures she had rejected, yet sobbing inwardly, regretful of being deprived of the warm, teasing companionship he had so fleetingly extended. She stole a quick glance at the man crouched over the wheel, noting once again the incredible physical likeness between himself and his twin. His clean-shaven face was grim, but earlier she had been fascinated by cheeks slashed with deep, humorous clefts whenever he grinned. And for most of the day his mouth had been kind ...

Hair the colour of rich autumn chestnuts, groomed to perfection, tapering down the length of his cheeks into rakish sideburns, copied Britt's style so exactly she could not help but wonder if he had been purposely imitative. All his life he had lived in the shadow of his brother's charm, envying him his gift of easy assurance, his ability to attract admiration as easily as a flame attracts moths. Raine caught a sharp breath. Could it be that today Thor had set out to prove something to himself? Might not the roughness of his approach have had its origins in experience and could the reluctance she had sensed have been caused by frustration born of deep shyness?

She screwed her eyes tightly shut to blot out the picture that had formed. Stamped on her mind was the image of a man—outwardly arrogant, inwardly shy—nerving himself to overcome his lack of confidence with the opposite sex only to be insulted and humiliated for his pains! Her remorse was so great she almost cried out, so intensely ashamed it was as much as she could do to withhold a plea for forgiveness and lack of understanding—a plea she had to hold back or else risk humiliating him further by betraying an insight into his innermost feelings . . .

CHAPTER EIGHT

VULCAN, fiercely resentful, and with tear-streaked face and mutinous, accusing eyes, rushed to meet them when the car swung into the drive. 'Where have you been?' he stormed. 'You might have taken me with you, I've had a dreadful day!'

At the sight of his quivering bottom lip Raine dropped her parcels and bent to give him a comforting hug. He responded by burying wet cheeks in her neck, his small arms tightening fit to choke.

Before she could attempt to soothe him, a storm erupted when Janice and Britt rounded the corner of the house in hot pursuit of their delinquent son.

'There you are, you horrible boy!' Janice raged, her cheeks an unbecoming red. Britt, his cool negligence completely routed, strode angrily forward, obviously intent upon administering punishment for some unknown misdeed, and Raine, feeling the small frame going alarmingly tense, immediately straightened and pushed Vulcan behind her for protection.

Britt halted in mid-stride, his eyebrows winging, then after seconds of surprised appraisal emitted a slow, incredulous whistle. 'What a transformation!' he murmured, his eyes kindling. 'I'm now beginning to understand my brother's haste to make you his wife.'

Janice seemed too nonplussed to speak. Her hard

glance raked Raine from head to foot, questioning her right to contrast so daintily cool, so femininely fetching, against her own heated dishevelment. Her look swung to Thor, and the jealousy she was feeling found release in a sneering taunt.

'So once again you're attempting to imitate your brother! Will you never learn that to look alike is not enough? Britt's charm is inherited from his mother, whereas you, Thor, have too much of your father in your make-up ever to achieve success with the opposite sex.'

Raine was slow to anger, but Janice's spiteful remarked provoked her into an action which in other circumstances she would not have dared to even contemplate. Thor was walking into the house, his set features gaining Janice no hint of satisfaction, when she ran forward and slipped a possessive arm into the crook of his elbow.

'How well you hide your talents, darling! Luckily for me, otherwise I might spend half my life fighting off other women. I'm very selfish, I much prefer having you all to myself!'

Her loving look caught him off guard. Green eyes flashed sparks as their glances held and for a long, breathless minute time stood still, the universe holding just the two of them—the only two that mattered!

She drowned in his green eyes, surfacing only long enough to encourage with a smile his decision to play up to their interested audience. He began by squeezing her hand, then, just when she was expecting a follow-up of empty words, his arm whipped around her waist and he bent to kiss her, a sweet, long, lingering kiss of ... *gratitude*? She was shaken when he released her, far too shaken to relinquish his supporting arm, so they walked together into the house with Vulcan close on their heels, leaving Britt and Janice to stew in their own discomfiture.

Vulcan poured out his troubles while Raine was unwrapping her parcels and stowing their contents into drawers and wardrobe. Seemingly, after breakfast, once having been notified of their absence, Janice had taken charge.

'She refused to let me go down to the stables because she thinks they're smelly,' Vulcan informed her with disgust. 'And Britt *agreed* with her!' This to his mind was the greatest anomaly of all.

Raine sighed. She had no wish to encourage the boy's attitude towards his parents, but the pair's selfishness did nothing to help further their cause.

'Then how did you spent the day?' she asked absently, brushing a soft swathe of chiffon against her cheeks.

'With stupid Plasticine, making stupid flowers an' stupid animals! Who wants to make clay animals when there are real ones outside in the fields?' he exploded.

Sensing that the worst was yet to come, she prompted, 'So then what did you do?'

'I skipped out when they weren't looking,' he admitted simply. 'Then we played a super game of hide and seek.'

'Your parents being the seekers, no doubt,' she concluded, picking up a tissue to hide her twitching lips.

He nodded. 'Right up until you and Thor arrived home. Why did you go without me?' His offhand question hid real hurt. 'I thought you liked me?'

'Oh, I do, darling, I do, but today Thor and I had business to attend to and had we taken you with us you would have been hopelessly bored. Besides,' she hesitated to voice the opinion, 'you ought really to be getting to know your parents better, they love you very much and you must learn to love them in return.'

'You don't *learn* to love like you learn reading and sums!' he scoffed with devastating logic. 'Love just *grows*!'

'Then you must give it time to grow,' she returned hastily, feeling herself in danger of becoming bogged down in unanswerable discussion. 'But right now it's time for your supper, run along downstairs, I'll pop in to see you when you are ready for bed.'

Love just grows! 'Out of the mouths of babes ...' Raine murmured as she sank down on the bed to examine at leisure her newly-discovered love for the Titian-haired giant. How had it come about, this great ache of tenderness, this desire to protect and cherish the man who hid his needs beneath a hide of tough aloofness? In any future confrontations she would need constantly to remind herself of his need of understanding; to soothe his arrogance with charm, to combat his anger with reason and to support him in every way she could against the abrasive qualities of his family.

She pressed a hot cheek against cool sheets, the

memory of the clumsy brutality of his first kiss erased by the storming gentleness of the second. Gratitude, of course, had motivated the impulsive embrace. By her display of loyalty, her hints of intimacy too cherished to be shared, by teasing him as only a loved one would dare, she had confused his enemies, thereby earning his passionless salute.

'Thor!' she whispered, searching the painfully blank ceiling, 'how can you be convinced that you are truly loved?'

She had almost finished dressing for dinner when there was a rap on the connecting door. A second later he entered, so assuredly that the suspicion grew that he was now regarding the favour more as a right than a privilege. Raine harnessed an impulse to smile, wary of betraying herself to the man she knew would shy from feminine advances as instinctively as a rabbit from a snare.

Consequently she was cool, merely nodding briefly before continuing the task of arranging her hair. Through the mirror she watched him as he prowled, sailor's strides, firm, purposeful, but within the confines of her room, advancing nowhere. His thoughts, it seemed, were similarly frustrating, because he paused as if to speak, then snapped his jaw and continued his restless pacing.

Her heart jerked, but she forced herself to ignore the brooding giant, unfamiliar in a dark dinner jacket that complemented perfectly his handsome, clean-shaven features and arrogantly held head.

'There's something I had intended to give you in York, but the opportunity didn't arise...' The staccato words jerked from his lips, startling her around to face him. He was holding an object in his huge fist, and as her puzzled eyes questioned he thrust it towards her, then strode across to the window leaving her clutching two minute boxes bound in white leather.

She knew what they continued before she opened them, but was not prepared for the breath-taking beauty of deep blue sapphires clustered around a diamond set in platinum and a wedding ring of broad gold inscribed 'Thor and Raine' followed by the date of her arrival at Danes' Dyke.

'Thor, why ... ?'

'They're a necessary part of the charade,' he clipped without turning.

'Perhaps, but much less expensive stones would have sufficed—these must have cost the earth, you'll not get back half what you paid for them when you come to resell...' She faltered at the thought, already in love with the twinkling baubles.

His frown lightened fractionally as he approached. 'Let's see if they fit.' His fingers felt cool against her wrist as he slid the wedding ring on to her third finger. For an unbearably intimate moment they stood looking silently down at the plain band that was an emblem of togetherness, of love and deep, abiding commitment. She stifled a sob, feeling a weight of regret and not a little shame. Deceit was abhorrent to her, but she had pledged her support and could not go back on her word.

'Thunder and rain,' he mused, 'two elements that have been wedded together since earth began —do you think you could withstand my turbulence for a lifetime, gentle Raine?'

To ease her constricted throat she choked out a laugh, grabbing at humour to protect her riotous feelings. He could be enjoying a jest at her expense, so a smoke-screen of unconcern was essential.

'Rain has a reputedly devastating effect even upon stone, its constant dripping has been known to change the shape of mountains ...'

'Then there's hope for me yet,' he answered gravely, 'provided you are agreeable to attempting the impossible?'

Her puzzlement required an explanation he seemed to find difficulty in framing. Clenched fists thrust deep into his pockets betrayed a nervousness completely alien, and a surge of colour accompanied words that jerked from his lips with acute embarrassment.

'What Janice said is quite true, I am an uncouth lout, at ease only in the company of men. I haven't known many women,' her heart lurched as he groped on, 'but what small experience I've had has taught me that they expect to be charmed and flattered and to have smooth courtesies extended by well-mannered escorts. Such things are beyond me,' he admitted simply. 'In the presence of women I become tongue-tied and clumsy—apt to spill drinks over dresses or tread on toes.' He paused, and Raine waited, unsure of the point he was trying to make yet loath to interrupt the heart-baring he was finding agonizing. 'That's why I'm asking for your help,' he rushed out the words, running a finger around the inside of his collar as if longing to rip the constriction from his neck.

To have pretended to misunderstand would have been cruel, so, although uncertain of the exact nature of his needs, she did not hesitate. 'I'll be glad to help in any way I can.'

His relief was tremendous. Immediately his large frame relaxed and the frown creasing his forehead disappeared as he sat down on the edge of her bed and smiled at her an invitation to join him. Cautiously she approached, wondering what further heartache lay in store, and discovered in the following seconds the enormity of the gulf between his feelings and her own.

'I felt sure you would understand. You're the only woman with whom I've ever been completely at ease, and with your help I'm sure I can overcome this stupid awkwardness that's prevented me from finding a wife.'

She went so still that he laughed, a self-deprecating sound holding no pretensions of mirth. 'Is the idea of my cherishing the same desires as other men so shocking?' he challenged. 'Believe me, the urge to feel the softness of a woman's body in my bed often keeps me awake at night! Desire is not confined to the Britts of this world—unattractive brutes such as myself are also blessed, or rather cursed, with sexual appetite.'

Raine strove to appear calm. His confession had shocked, not because it betrayed desire but because it betrayed lack of desire—*for love*. Carefully she chose her words. 'Is that all marriage means to you, a woman to share your bed, a means of satisfying an appetite? Don't you think...' she stumbled in her distress, 'you ought to seek more than physical compatibility from any woman with whom you propose to share your life?'

She did not blame him solely for the puzzlement he portrayed. He had never known the influence of a loving mother or felt part of a family united by happy, caring parents. His father had become embittered of the woman who had borne his sons and had sown seeds of contempt in the mind of a youth who, now a man, was left grappling with the bitter harvest.

'I don't think so,' he frowned.

She gave up. The issue was far too complex. 'Oh, very well, what exactly do you want me to do?'

He pushed aside her vexing poser to concentrate on an explanation. 'Being a woman, you're bound to be aware of my shortcomings, and what I'd like you to do is point out where I go wrong. For instance,' he edged nearer, warming to his subject, 'this afternoon when I kissed you—what was it that caused you to turn on me like an outraged virgin?' Noting her sweep of confused colour, he hastened to add, 'I'm casting no reflection upon you, you were probably perfectly justified in reacting the way you did, but I'd like to understand why. What is it about me that women find repulsive?'

'You're not repulsive!' she gasped, indignant on his behalf.

'Then what?' he persisted with such blind helplessness she was forced to be truthful.

'Your ... your approach is all wrong,' she stammered, wishing he would stop willing her to continue.

'Yes, I've gathered that much, but *how* is it wrong?'

'It's rather difficult to explain,' she floundered.

'Tell you what!' He shifted nearer and with dead-pan seriousness slipped an arm around her waist. 'I'll proceed exactly as I did this afternoon, then when I reach the point where my tactics begin to offend you call a halt and we'll begin dissecting from there.'

Raine stared, unable to believe her ears. With any other man she would immediately have suspected an ulterior motive, but Thor was so unpractised in the art of seduction that such a theory was rendered unthinkable.

With nautical thoroughness he proceeded step by step to duplicate his actions. Tentatively, he ruffled her hair, seeming to find much pleasure in fingering the soft dark cloud framing piquant features brushed by sudden shyness. Slowly his head lowered until his mouth, wearing the suspicion of a smile, was hovering above her lips as hesitantly as a bee over the fragile petals of a flower. 'May I ...?' he breathed, awaiting her permission.

She nodded and closed her eyes. His arm tightened, pulling her nearer and nearer until her heart was pounding against his muscular chest, but still the kiss was delayed.

Shyly her arms crept upwards until her fingers found and entwined around strands of fiery hair. She lifted her lips, hungry for contact, every nerve straining for release from the tension built up by his insistence upon this form of clinical analysis. His breath fell hot upon her cheek, his touch seared through her flimsy dress, igniting passion from her and from him a quick, muffled imprecation against the sound of the dinner gong intruding its summons from downstairs.

The width of the room was between them when she opened her eyes. Bemusedly she watched him thumbing his empty pipe, too overwrought to wonder at the fact that his knuckles were standing out white on hands far from steady.

'So far so good!' His hearty cheerfulness shook her quivering nerves. 'At least we now know that the preliminaries were not at fault, the rest of our investigation must wait until later.'

Raine managed to nod as she walked towards the door. She never wanted to find herself in the same painful situation again, but to tell him so would arouse his curiosity and she felt she would rather die than allow him to suspect her senseless infatuation.

Pride made her appear more beautiful than she knew. In a dress pink as spring buds, she swirled passed him and was held, teetering on the toes of silken slippers, when his hand shot out to grip her slender wrist.

'You're not regretting your promise to help groom me for matrimony?'

The question was almost her undoing, but she weathered his gimlet glance, feeling sudden affinity with a harpooned whale. 'I'm not altogether certain you're in need of help,' she countered, 'nevertheless, my promise still stands.'

With much satisfaction, Thor stowed away his pipe, then hooked her arm into the crook of his elbow to escort her downstairs. 'You're a real sport!' The accolade caused her a pained wince. 'Not many women would accept the role of guinea-pig in such an experiment. However, the course I've plotted should yield some compensations. I've decided that the experience I need can't be gained here at Danes' Dyke, we must move farther afield. Courtship—or in our case, the practising of it—calls for an atmosphere of soft lights, music, exotic food and secluded alcoves conducive to exploratory skirmishes, don't you agree? I believe there are one or two such places in the vicinity, I'll find out their exact location, then perhaps tomorrow evening we can dine out?'

The statement was framed as a question but needed no answer, so she did not bother to reply. She was a mere pawn in the game he had devised to capture himself a wife. Captain Thor, master-mariner, had charted a course through dangerous waters and would heed not one word of warning about the folly of sailing through unfamiliar shallows. She knew exactly the type of woman that would appeal to him—beautiful, sophisticated, superficial and completely without depth. The sort of woman his brother favoured, the sort his father had favoured. *Would Halden men never learn?*

'Britt and Janice will think you've gone completely mad,' was all the protest she allowed herself.

He stopped, peering through the gloom of a darkened passageway to seek the source of the dejected voice. She sensed his grin and longing swamped her, a longing to be the object of his search, a terrible, sweet yearning to know the ecstasy of becoming his wife, a desire to protect him from the rejection that was bound to follow any attempt to woo modern woman in the manner of his lusty Viking ancestors.

'Do you know, I think perhaps I *am* a little mad,' he teased through the darkness.

Some instinct caused her to tense, but too late. He scooped her slight body high into his arms, hitched one leg across the banister and began sliding down the staircase. Alarm and delight rioted in her veins as she clung to him, panic-stricken yet, conversely, unafraid. Breathless with laughter, he deposited her in the hallway, still retaining his grip on her waist while wickedly he reminded her, 'The lunatic and the lover, my dear, are of imagination all compact!'

CHAPTER NINE

BRITT and Janice were in the sitting-room sipping pre-dinner drinks while they waited for Thor and Raine to join them. Janice had obviously gone to a lot of a trouble to compete with the girl she had once written off as a nonentity; her body was fitted snugly as a dagger into a sheaf of stiff black gros-grain that left marble shoulders bare and drew immediate attention to blonde hair coiled into an intricate coronet.

Against Raine's fresh young beauty, however, she appeared stiffly formal, and the suspicion that she was overdressed for the small family gathering did nothing to sweeten her temper. Predictably, it was Thor who drew her fire, his dancing eyes and humour-quirked mouth drawing her venom.

'Ah, Prince Charming! What changes you have wrought in him, my dear Raine—don't tell me mere kisses changed the frog into a prince—or am I getting my fairy tales a trifle mixed?'

'It happens,' Thor returned easily. 'I find it difficult myself to dissociate the ugly sister from whichever character it was whose every spoken word came out as a writhing sake.' Urbanely, he poured out drinks, then sauntered across to Raine, calming her anxiety with a conspiratorial grin.

Britt frowned his wife to silence before addressing a peeved request to his brother. 'If ever again you intend disappearing for the day you might let us know so that arrangements can be made for someone to take charge of Vulcan. It was a bit much,' he blustered, 'your calmly walking out and leaving us to cope with an unruly brat whose behaviour was, to say the least, diabolical!'

Thor's eyebrows shot up. 'We thought we were doing you a favour! Didn't you say you intended to become better acquainted with your son?'

'Well, yes...' Britt seemed nonplussed by the reminder. His feathers had been ruffled as never before by his wayward son and already he was regretting giving in to his wife's spurious impulse to claim the child they hardly knew. 'But gradually. I refuse to be pitchforked into fatherhood——'

'As I was!' Thor's head tilted. 'How very sensible of you!'

Resentment seethed between the two men—so physically alike yet so basically different. Britt, who up until then had had everything his own way, seemed unable to grasp that the charm that had eased his path through life was no longer working upon the brother who had resigned himself from childhood to being an also-ran, a colourless reflection of his flamboyant twin.

Raine felt unbearably agitated, violence was heaving beneath the surface, an explosive force seeking the relief of one tiny spark. Then the crack of splintering glass shattered the silence and dumbly she stared at the spread of wine across the floor, unaware that the glass was hers, crushed by tense fingers. Thor spun round with a muttered curse. Swiftly he crossed to her side and grasped her

111

shaking hands in his huge fist, speaking gently to soothe away the tension caused by fear.

'Don't worry,' he urged, 'nothing is about to erupt, I promise you.'

Even in the midst of turmoil she was conscious of Janice's sharp glance and the question that rapped across the room was a warning to them both that her curiosity was aroused.

'In which part of Ireland did you live, Raine—I don't believe the exact location was ever established?' For an infinitesimal second a picture flashed across her mind, a cameo of rolling hills swathed in mist, a large red-brick house surrounded by fields in which horses and cattle grazed contentedly upon grass that was vividly green ...

'In Belfast,' Thor supplied briefly.

Just in time, she stopped herself from contradicting.

But Janice seemed to have lost interest. 'How dreadful for you!' she shuddered. 'I'm not surprised your parents are in no hurry to return.'

Dinner was a ritual suffered for the most part in silence. Raine toyed with the food on her plate, still preoccupied with the flash of memory that had yielded a tantalizing glimpse of what might have been her home or what could merely have been an unconnected image, the sort any mind might fasten upon at the mention of Ireland. When she pushed away her untouched plate Thor caught her eye and smiled. Tremulously the corners of her mouth lifted and the action seemed to propel him into a sudden decision. He stood up to walk behind her, and with his hands resting on the back of her chair politely asked Britt and Janice to excuse them both.

'It's been a long day for both of us. Raine is tired and obviously not hungry, so if you don't mind, we'll leave you to finish dinner alone. By the way,' he flung across his shoulder when they reached the door, 'we shall be out all day tomorrow. We'll take Vulcan with us, but one or both of you will have to look after him during the evening as Raine and I will be dining out.'

Britt's look of affront was so marked it was an effort to remain straight-faced until the door had closed behind them, but once they were alone Raine, encouraged by Thor's wide grin, gave way to stifled laughter.

'What shall we do now?' she gurgled. 'I enjoyed the grand exit, but it's still a little early for bed.'

'I know of something that might interest you— come with me.'

Obediently she followed him along a passageway until they reached a door of solid oak hung on heavy iron hinges with a lock that squealed a protest when Thor turned the huge key he unearthed from its hiding place. 'No one ever comes in here but me,' he explained, closing the door behind them as if relieved to break contact with the outside world. 'This is my escape hole, once inside I can lose myself in my hobby and forget all frustrations.'

Feeling very much aware of the honour bestowed, Raine waited while he groped his way through pitch black darkness, then after the scraping of a match an oil lamp flooded light on to the bare stone walls of what had originally been a cellar, now converted into a workshop with lathes and workbenches littered with drills and miscellaneous tools. When she stepped forward Thor pointed to a pile of brown-coloured stones heaped upon the workbench. 'That is the material I work with, can you guess what it is?'

Gingerly, she ran her finger along a sharp edge. 'Flint ... ?' she ventured.

He shook his head. 'First let me show you some of the finished products, then you'll be better able to guess.' Out of a drawer he pulled a box, an old-fashioned jewellery case, its leather covering tattered with age. Inside, red velvet lining looking as good as new afforded a perfect backcloth for jewellery fashioned out of glittering black stone. He lifted out a necklace of intricately carved beads supporting a diamond-cut pendant and Raine accepted it wordlessly, unable to associate work of such delicacy with the man who had freely confessed to being awkward and clumsy.

'*You* made this?' she breathed, entranced by the sparkling black gems. 'But what is the connection between this necklace and that pile of stones?'

'Jet,' he corrected. 'Those stones are just as they were when they were picked up from the beach, all that's needed is cutting and polishing to bring out their true colour.'

'Picked up from the beach? You mean the jet is just lying there waiting to be picked up by anyone?'

'Anyone who can recognize it as such,' he confirmed. 'Unfortunately quite a lot of tourists are exploited by unscrupulous locals who sell lumps of coal as genuine jet. All that glisters——' he shrugged. 'You know the rest.'

Raine glanced from the pile of dull stones to the beautifully finished necklace and sensed he was comparing himself with Britt—to his own detriment.

'How clever you are, Thor! Transforming mediocrity into beauty is a talent you possess in abundance—as I ought to know.' She pirouetted in her new dress, making her meaning obvious.

Hard fingers bit into her arm, spinning her round so that she was forced to meet eyes of glittering green. 'Elfin blue eyes, hair black as a pixie's and a mouth an angel might envy could never be considered mediocre! You're as unique as this jet,' he brooded down, 'and as beneficial to all who need your help.' She trembled; although the cellar was unheated her body felt feverish. Mistaking the tremor for fear, he released her and swung away with the matter-of-fact observation, 'There are many superstitions connected with jet. Once it was used as a means of warding off the evil eye. It was also reputed to cure dropsy, epilepsy, snakebite and the pains of childbirth, but the most remarkable claim ever recorded,' his shadow loomed back out of the darkness, 'is that it has the power to erase the agony of "virgin purity by lust defiled".'

She stiffened, disturbed by the mockery of his words. She could not understand his unpredictable changes of mood, one minute morose, the next deliberately provoking. Black-browed displeasure she could cope with, but these flashes of teasing charm left her feeling unbearably buffeted. Was he *practising* again?

She edged away, hiding her nervousness behind a flippant reply. 'Fortunately, I'm not likely to suffer from any of those ailments—especially not the latter, so—in my case—the use of jet as a talisman could hardly be justified.'

'How can you be sure?' Carelessly he played with her emotions. 'You're fully aware of my needs.'

'I *am* sure!' She twirled away, her heart thumping, resenting the ease with which he could set her pulses racing.

His short laugh put an end to the verbal dalliance. Taking pity on her confusion, he fell back upon the mundane. 'These tools are not unlike those used by prehistoric jet workers, varied a little in shape, perhaps, but still basically similar.'

'How . . . how do you make the holes through the beads?' She grasped the subject gratefully.

'With this.' He chose a drill from the collection littering his workbench. 'Force would shatter the jet to pieces, and burning a way through would be equally disastrous. One needs to know about the nature of rough jet from the start—where the spar begins and ends, how the seam runs—without that knowledge the resulting piece would show flaws and lack the clear, bright surface some people liken to black amber.'

'Sea amber!' Her imagination was fired.

'Not quite,' he corrected with a smile. 'It has been established that jet is really driftwood which has been subjected to chemical action in stagnant water, then afterwards flattened by enormous pressure. So it's in the cliffs that consist of layers of shale and rock and solidified mud of an ancient sea where the jet is found. The stones found on the beach are mostly chippings from fallen rock and are not, as you would like to believe, jewels washed up from the sea.'

'I see.' She was disappointed. 'So jet can actually be mined?'

'And was for many years,' he nodded. 'At one time, the industry flourished around these parts, keeping many men employed. Unfortunately, the demand for jet diminished, then faded almost completely. Only one of the genuine old craftsmen still survives, and it was he who taught me the necessary skills.'

'So where do you get your jet?' she demanded, utterly absorbed.

'I'll show you tomorrow,' he promised. 'There's a cove along the coast which in the past has yielded quite generous amounts from cliff falls, but the easiest pieces to work are those that are washed and rounded by the action of the sea scouring them among the sand and shingle of the shore. Even when one knows what to look for they're not easy to find. Still, with your help, and Vulcan's, I should reap quite a good haul. We might even find the time to visit Tommy Tose—the old jet carver I mentioned. These days, he's too unsteady on his pins to get down to the beach, but as he likes to "keep his hand in" he's always grateful for a supply of rough jet.'

'I would like that.' Interest in a glass-fronted

cabinet tucked away in a corner was responsible for her absent reply. She gravitated towards it, drawn instinctively by a tantalizing glimpse of the unusual. 'May I ...' She awaited permission to pry and was rewarded by a nod. Carefully she manoeuvred open the door to examine the contents of the dusty shelves.

'Oh, Thor!' Her cry held admiration and reproof. On the shelves, in jumbled disarray, were carvings of unique beauty veiled by cobwebs and dust. Casting him a look of resigned impatience, she grabbed a rag from the workbench and reached inside the cabinet to retrieve a miniature table carved from jet, its circular top daintily scalloped around the edges, an engraved stem splaying outwards into four paws with claws outspread. A matching tray holding two cut-jet decanters and tiny glasses delighted her and she succumbed to a childish urge to lift one of the miniature stoppers and pretend to pour wine into the doll-sized glasses.

'Pray, good sir, may I offer you a drink?'

'Thank you,' he accepted, a humorous quirk playing around his lips. With only two fingers he completely engulfed the small glass and the resulting comparison was so funny she collapsed into laughter. Ruefully, he grinned, acknowledging the joke against his huge hands and the contradictory fragility of the objects they had fashioned.

Then suddenly her humour fled. A giant yearning over fragility no longer struck her as funny.

She reached out to touch him, feeling an ache to communicate the sympathy that was making her heart swell. 'Such competent hands,' she murmured, spreading her fingers wide across his knuckles, 'yet so wonderfully artistic. You're a mass of contradictions, Thor, one moment ruthless, the next gentle; terrifying as a bellow, soothing as a whisper; a bruising grip healed by a soothing caress. Confusing, complex creature—never so strong than when you are gentle, never so gentle as when you are in a position of strength...'

Swinging mere inches above his head, a lamp turned his red hair to copper. Beneath its beam they were trapped in a magic circle, silently exploring, each uncertain of the other's mind. As he studied her small, serious face a flame flared in the depths of his eyes, then was quickly extinguished, and as if at a painful reminder he flinched and broke the spell by moving away.

'Your sweet tongue could change the direction of a elephant,' he grated, 'but you ought never to allow misguided sympathy to tempt you into potentially dangerous situations, otherwise you could be sorry —you might even have reason to resort to the much-disparaged powers ancients accorded to talismans of jet!'

Fire raced into her cheeks. He was accusing her of flirting, and his words were a warning of what to expect from a man grown eager to hold a woman in his arms. *She* was a woman, but for practising purposes only! Miserable tears stung her eyes.

'All I was trying to do,' she controlled a wayward sob, 'was show my admiration of your many talents. After all, not many men have the ability to run a farm, bring up a child single-handed, skipper a ship, engrave wonderful——'

He interrupted her with an angry hiss. 'Sailors are taught to be resourceful, Miss Naïve. But as they are also noted philanderers, do you think it was wise to try to tempt one of them into taking advantage?'

'How dare you!' She forced a small flash of temper. 'In any case, how could I? You've said often enough how impossible you find women—you even asked me to teach you to feel at ease in their company, remember?'

'I remember,' he countered inscrutably. 'And you're doing such an able job I find the exercise becoming easier by the minute!'

CHAPTER TEN

In order to reach the bay where the jet was usually to be found, they travelled a short distance across the moors to join the coast road, then after a few miles they turned right, down a narrow dyke-lined lane leading directly to the sea. Raine was pointing out to Vulcan the outline of a large ship just visible on the horizon when suddenly the ground seemed to drop from beneath them. They had breasted a rise, and instead of continuing straight the road dipped at such an acute angle they seemed poised, high and precariously, on the edge of the world. She and Vulcan held their breath as Thor engaged low gear and began manoeuvring the car forward. Below, the small crescent-shaped bay, its houses clinging like nests along protective cliffs, could have been a toy town viewed by air and the solidly substantial Range Rover an aircraft winging a cautious way down the line of cliff in search of a landing place.

No one spoke until Thor swung the car into a car park placed strategically at the bottom of the hill to eliminate the very real danger of cars nose-diving into the sea. 'Whew! That was super, Uncle Thor, can we do it again ... ?'

'Were you afraid?' Thor questioned, his eyes on Raine. 'I could have warned you, but I decided it would be a shame to spoil the excitement of a first descent. Did I do wrong?'

She marshalled her scattered wits and gasped, 'I don't think I've ever flown, but I imagine the sensation must be similar. I thought at first we'd gone straight over the edge of the cliff,' she admitted shakily, 'it hardly seemed possible for the car to remain on the road.'

Vulcan shot off towards the cliffs while she waited until Thor had secured the car. They had parked practically on the beach, so the houses and shops that comprised the small village were behind them, rising in tiers up the cliff side, connected by steep flights of steps or cobbled paths, some of them with handrails to assist the ascent.

'You don't have to be a mountain goat to live here, but it helps,' Thor quipped to Raine, reminded of an amazed pygmy surveying Everest. 'Tommy Tose's cottage is perched almost on the cliff top, but I promise you the ascent isn't half so formidable as it looks. However, you can judge for yourself later, after we've found our jet.'

They followed Vulcan's footprints across firm sand slashing a golden pathway between lazy, foam-curled waves and a carpet of boulders and rock clustered at the foot of towering cliffs. They could see his figure in the distance, bent double in his search for treasure, his small hands shovelling finds deep into trouser pockets.

'Oh, no!' Thor groaned. 'Hurry, let's catch that young man up, otherwise I'll be spending best part of the day sorting out his indiscriminate finds.' He grabbed her hand and began to run, his long legs twice outreaching her stride. She laughed a protest, but then had to save her breath for the effort of keeping up as, leaving her barely time to touch toes to sand, he propelled her along the beach with powerful impetus.

When he released her she collapsed laughing at Vulcan's feet, but the boy was too engrossed to be sidetracked by the frivolous behaviour of adults who, in his opinion, ought to be showing more dedication to the task in hand. Quickly he plunged a hand into his pocket. 'I've found lots, Uncle Thor! Look at this enormous piece—and what do you think of this ... ?'

Raine loved Thor anew when he squatted on his heels to give serious consideration to the pile of glass, shale, slate and coal Vulcan deposited hopefully on the sand. He picked up one of the larger pieces, studied it, then scraped its surface with a pocket knife before gravely offering his opinion.

'I'm afraid none of this is much use, old son. It *is* jet,' he lied hastily when Vulcan's face fell, 'but of a quality not quite up to standard.' The sun burned a halo of gold around each of the two heads bent together in serious discussion and in that moment Raine felt a surge of pure happiness. She wanted to hug each of them, the red-haired giant and the young Viking who could have been his son, but the impulse had to be curbed—and not merely because she had no right to intrude upon the business of men!

'You must understand,' Thor continued, 'that for some people—the "jetties", for instance, who spend their time combing the beach—these stones might suffice. But for the really dedicated collectors such as Tommy Tose and myself only the best will do. This is a sample of what I want you to look for.' He took a dingy brown stone from his pocket. 'See how easily the outer skin scrapes off showing a black sparkle underneath? Here, try it with this penknife, but mind you go carefully, no slashed fingers or cut knees!'

'Do you think he's responsible enough to be allowed a knife?' Raine whispered, casting a worried look at Vulcan's enraptured face.

'Surely,' he frowned, 'I'm not such a fool as to pass on responsibility without ensuring the presence of the discretion that goes with it. You must learn to trust him,' he directed impatiently. 'If you treat the boy like a man he'll act like a man!'

Raine would have argued the folly of expecting wisdom from an infant, but the day was too glorious, so she contented herself with keeping a close watch on Vulcan, who surprised her by making mature use of the disputed penknife.

Coastal erosion had left exposed strata of rock on the cliff face and the seeking of the 'jet rock' described by Thor became more and more fascinating and less of a game as the day wore on. Rough seas had gouged the cliff, leaving holes like eyeless sockets out of which a head would pop at intervals to call Thor's attention to a promising find. By the time they were ready for lunch a pile of stones satisfying enough to win Thor's approval was heaped upon the sand and quizzing their flushed, expectant faces he congratulated them with a smile, 'Well done, shipmates, you've done me proud! Wait here while I fetch your reward.'

He strode off to fetch the picnic basket from the car and Raine relaxed upon the sand, warmed by exertion, by a benevolent sun, and by Thor's unthinking charm. When he forgot to be cautious he was devastating, far more so than Britt, whose practised style was apt to jar. Today, it seemed, he had managed to forget that she was a woman and was treating her as a friend. *Shipmate!* She did not wonder that crews were reputedly willing to follow him to the ends of the earth!

Her blushing confusion when she opened her eyes and saw him towering above her almost gave her away, and his thoughtful look as he watched her hands trembling as she set out the food stiffened her resolve never to allow her thoughts to drift again into such dangerous currents.

'Pasty?' she offered, a striving to appear calm.

'Thank you.' He took a man-sized bite, his eyes questioning her heightened colour. 'If you feel it's warm enough, perhaps later we can have a swim?'

She hesitated. 'I don't think I will, thank you all the same . . .'

'Why ever not?'

'I don't know how.'

'Good lord!' the sea Viking expressed his disgust. 'That situation must be remedied.'

Raine felt desperate reluctance as she scanned the sea's surface, suspecting menace beneath the concealing waves. 'But I don't want the situation to be remedied,' she gulped.

While he digested her refusal, Vulcan, with the unthinking cruelty of the young, jumped to his feet with the scoffing chant, 'Cowardy, cowardy custard, Raine's afraid of the sea!'

'Be quiet, you spalpeen!' she rounded on him, with a flash of Irish, 'not everyone is as conversant as yourself with miles of water, or wants to be!'

For once she rendered them both speechless. Up until then spirit and temper had been notably absent from her character; fear of the unknown was behind her heated reaction.

Thor was quick to understand. Although his eyes twinkled, his voice was grave when he reminded Vulcan,

'Who was it who ran in terror from the offer of a ride in a "chopper" when the Fleet Air Arm dropped in on us unexpectedly?'

Vulcan was immediately deflated. 'I was much younger then,' he sulked, scuffing his toes in the sand.

'It *was* all of three months ago,' Thor agreed, poker-faced.

Suddenly the heavy silence was broken by his laughter, such hearty, unrestrained laughter coming from a man whose aloof demeanour had previously allowed no more than a faint smile or a swift grin. But he was rolling on his back in a paroxysm of mirth, his flaying arms a constant annoyance to the colony of gulls whose greedy eyes were fixed upon the remains of his discarded pasty. Then minutes later Vulcan succumbed and as they both seemed in danger of expiring each time they glanced her way, Raine's outraged expression gradually softened until finally she, too, was forced to join in.

They stretched out on the beach, spent but

happy, subduing a still-active humour that now and then threatened to overspill. 'Would either of you like more to eat?' Raine questioned, daring them to laugh.

'No, thank you,' Thor's mouth gave a treacherous twitch, 'as we've taken so long over lunch we'll have to move sharply if we want to visit Tommy Tose. We're dining out tonight, remember?'

How could she forget! Hastily she began repacking the basket, her fingers moving as swiftly as her chaotic thoughts. She did not want to dine tête-à-tête with this unleashed stranger, she fretted, their lessons were progressing so quickly and so well that teacher was in danger of being overtaken by the pupil. How could she possibly remain aloof enough to instruct him in the art of making himself pleasing to women when her eyes insisted upon clinging to his, her body ached for his touch and his deep-timbred voice sounded heavenly music in her ears? If only he would stick to his rigidly unbending rules she could cope, but he was as restless as the sea she feared—as deep, as deceptive and just as overwhelmingly unpredictable!

Tommy Tose's cottage was as enchanting as others they passed on their climb from the beach. Every few steps along the way they were halted by sights unusual or eye-catching; miniature gardens patchworked with poppies, roses, geraniums, irises and fuchsias; old ships' lanterns hung outside sturdy oak doors; house names painted on small buoys—Spray Cottage, Lobster Pot. The Crow's Nest. Now and then an opening between houses beckoned, inviting the curious to pry, and after squeezing through a space so narrow Thor had to negotiate it sideways, a vista opened up of sea, sky and cliff, blissfully calm, but reminding by way of sea-soaked rock, and seaweed strewn high above high water mark, of havoc caused on other less benevolent days.

The cottage had a thatched roof, whitewashed walls hung with wire baskets full of geraniums, and tiny windowpanes made of thick, uneven glass through which everything looked rainbow tinged and slightly distorted. Vulcan, obviously sure of his welcome, ran through the half open door straight into the main living quarters, a treasure chest of a place crammed with bric-à-brac preserved from youth by a man who could have been a hundred years old.

As Raine hesitated on the threshold Thor pushed her forward. 'I've brought a friend with me, Tommy, I've told her so much about your craft she's dying to see for herself the work that's made you famous.'

'Famous?' The word amused him. With teeth clenched around the stem of a very mature pipe, he reproved, 'Those days are gone, Master Thor, there ain't nobody much interested in jet these days. Once, it had its royal and noble patrons, old Queen Victoria did much to help the trade when she introduced jet into court circles. After the death of her beloved Albert she deemed the black jewellery suitable for mourning, so then the industry flourished. But later on demand lessened—fashions change regardless of the livelihoods of men . . .' The opinion was expressed without rancour, but his withered, deeply-lined face was momentarily sad. His eyes brightened, however, when they alighted upon Raine, recognizing sympathy, understanding and a love of all things ancient in her expressive face.

'Come along in, my dear, don't just stand there, any friend of Master Thor's is especially welcome!'

'Thank you.' She stepped inside. 'What an interesting home you have—such a feast of unusual objects.'.

He beamed his approval. 'Go ahead, look to your heart's content while I make us all a cup of tea.'

'I'll do that,' Thor insisted. 'You sit there and prepare yourself for innumerable questions.' Nothing loath, the old man settled back in his chair while Thor went in search of a teapot. A little shyly at first Raine sauntered around, peering at stuffed fish imprisoned behind glass, tapping a nervous fingernail against the side of a jar inside which a strange sea serpent was preserved in alcohol, becoming absorbed in glass paperweights that rained showers of snow upon churches or villages immediately they were upturned. Then Pasch eggs caught her eye—gilt-painted, the names of their recipients written boldly in black, and bearing the dates that showed aeons had passed since the offerings had first been clutched in small excited hands.

Vulcan was settled at the old man's feet listening avidly to some tale when Thor came back carrying a laden tray. Raine watched as he put it down, then carried a teapot across to the fireplace where a black, soot-encrusted kettle was singing on a hook suspended over the open fire. Gingerly he tipped it sideways and water spluttered along the hot spout and into the teapot with a hiss that promised a nectar far divorced from the product of modern tea-bags. Minutes later they were sitting around the fire supping the brew, strong, sweet, laced with cream and tasting not one whit less enjoyable because in its aroma was contained the very minutest trace of soot.

'I love it here!' Vulcan startled her by putting her thoughts into words. 'I feel history is all around us.' He struggled to convey an impression. 'Live history, I mean, not the dreary stuff we learn from books.'

Tommy sipped slowly from his mug. 'Aye, you could well be right. I've lived too long, that's my trouble! I can remember the day each of the things in this cottage was bought, yet you young 'uns must look upon them as a load of rubbish.'

'Of course we don't!' Raine spoke as indignantly as she felt. 'Your possessions are old and beautifully cared for as well as being mostly unique.' She faltered, made shy by Thor's warm smile.

'Sooner or later age makes everything unique,' the old man replied, but she saw he was pleased.

'Which reminds me,' Thor cut in. 'We found quite a bit of rough jet on the beach, so we've brought you some—enough to last you throughout the winter, I dare say.'

Tommy jerked upright. 'That's good news! The ladies from the Institute are always after jet ornaments round about Christmas time and I don't like having to disappoint 'em.' His fingers flexed around the stones, eager to explore the possibilities of shape and structure, and Raine glimpsed the enormity of pleasure he received from his work, now relegated to a hobby.

'May I play with the ships?' Vulcan piped hopefully. 'I promise to handle them carefully.'

'Bless you, lad, don't you always? I told you last time you've no need to ask—jump to it, you know where they're kept!'

Vulcan scrambled to his feet and ran to open a cupboard out of which he carefully manoeuvred a large box which he set down on the carpet. Thor was discussing the merits of the jet with Tommy, who was handling the stones with expert fingers, so only Raine shared his pleasure as he lifted each model out of the box.

Perfectly appointed, every detail painstakingly carved out of shining black stone, the flotilla of vessels was laid out reverently on the mat.

'This is a yawl, this one here is a lugger, and that's a coble,' he pointed out, proud of his knowledge. 'Real cobles are built out of naturally bent wood—not steamed into shape like other boats—in the same way the Vikings built their long boats—isn't that so, Mr Tose?' He raised his voice to attract the old man's attention.

'Aye, lad, it is. The coble has a high, narrow bow and a low draught aft when the rudder is unshipped; they were designed for beach landing, and can negotiate waters impassable to all but a lifeboat.'

Dreamily, Raine stared at the distinctive craft, imagining it cleaving its way through alien seas packed stem to stern with fearless Vikings flaunting their traditional flag bearing the image of a plundering, sharp-eyed raven.

She was brought back to earth with a bump by Vulcan's impatient prod, and was immediately captured in the sights of the present-day Viking opposite who was paying less attention than he ought to his companion. Feeling the scorch of a blush, she averted her eyes, seizing upon Vulcan's words as a lifeline.

'This one's a model of the whaler Mr Tose's grandfather used to sail in, isn't it super?'

'It . . . it looks very functional.' She cast around in her mind for something more to say, not wanting to show it less favour than she had shown the others.

'Whalers had to be, my dear,' the old man defended, 'both the ships and the men who sailed in them! Frills and fancy paintwork would have been of little use in a fierce nor'-easterly, or in Arctic waters where mountainous seas left decks awash with ice and the wind was cutting enough to remove the skin from a man's face without his even being aware of it. Yes, a lot of work went into the designing of that ship,' he mused, 'most of it done by Master Thor's great-grandfather, old Captain Halden himself! He was a superb seaman, often when I was a boy I listened to my grandfather telling tales of his exploits—he sailed with him on many voyages.' His old eyes watered as he peered back into the past. 'And many's the hour I've stood with my grandmother on the cliff top keeping lookout for the first sighting of the whaling fleet returning home. Many were wasted hours,' he reflected, 'but what a heartening sight it was when eventually the first ship was spotted with the jawbone of its best whale hoisted on its lower spars and a huge garland hanging from the mast! Oh, but you've heard enough of me blethering for one day!' He startled them back into the present. 'Let's all have another cup of tea.'

Half an hour later they bade the old man a reluctant goodbye and set off down the cliff path with his pleas for an early return visit ringing in their ears. Vulcan skipped on ahead, and with Thor's hand supporting her elbow Raine felt a surge of happiness that recompensed fully for having had to abandon the tranquillity of a more peaceful age.

'No need to ask if you enjoyed your visit.' Thor sounded slightly amused, but she did not mind his awareness of her vulnerability to the romance of earlier years—especially to stories concerning his family's exciting, danger-ridden past. With a history such as his, and with the blood of adventurers and explorers mingling in his veins, it seemed inconceivable that he should be content with his present lot.

'Don't you ever feel frustrated, Thor?' She turned to face him, her dark eyes melting with concern.

Eyebrows shot up over eyes glinting at the dangerous question, but his satirical smile faded before her guileless, innocent expression.

'How you *do* fret about the feelings of others,' he chided, softly savage. 'Yes, there are times when I feel frustrated, times when I feel trapped in a sinking ship, with no lifeboat to hand, just a rail to hang on to while the water slowly rises and the ship threatens to overturn trapping me inside!'

'Oh!' Her lips formed a gasp of alarm, Appalled by the turmoil. her question had uncovered, she began to stammer an apology, but firm fingers stilled her lips and whimsy played around his mouth while softly he assured her, 'But not today, infant! Today's voyage has been calm and peaceful, no rough water nor high seas—today I even glimpsed fulfilment in my future self.'

CHAPTER ELEVEN

HOURS later, bathed, dressed and impatiently waiting, Raine was still sifting through his words, pondering on their meaning. They had seemed to imply some measure of contentment, even happiness—if such a word could be applied to a person as complex as Thor—and the idea lent added dimension to the proposed dinner engagement. Although perfectly contented during the past weeks of voluntary drudgery, she was young and vital enough to feel excitement at the prospect of dining in a fashionable restaurant escorted by a presentable male, however unflattering his motives, so, even though her presence was to be primarily functional, she had taken pains to ensure he would not find fault with her appearance.

She ran across to the mirror to make a last-minute inspection and projected a smile of satisfaction at the image presented by the fly-blown glass. Against a background of dark walls and heavy furniture her slender figure seemed captured inside a floating golden cloud. Softly clinging nylon swathed smooth white shoulders and against a youthful curve of neck soot-black hair curled into tender fronds. Her deep blue eyes clouded momentarily with doubt, then, encouraged by a mouth that refused to despair, regained their natural sparkle. At the same time a dimple appeared low in her cheek, happy, elusive and immensely fetching.

Her absorption was so complete she missed Thor's knock and was startled almost out of her wits when his image loomed out of the background to join hers within the circle of glass. Their glances held, and for long seconds their faces were framed as if in a locket of remembrance—a moment captured, to be treasured always.

Swiftly she turned, unable to bear the torment of wishful thinking, and blundered straight into the rock-hard body that was so much closer than she had imagined.

'Steady!' He sounded tolerantly amused. 'I'd hate to see all that finery disarranged.' His roving eyes assessed her. 'I'm flattered that you have gone to so much trouble simply to please me—no woman has ever done so before.'

'To assist in your education!' She disguised nervousness with flippancy. 'Continue exercising such flattery and women will begin beating a path to your door!'

His breathed reply sounded like: 'Heaven forbid!' but she could not be sure. In any case, it was highly unlikely that he would reject the very outcome for which he was aiming.

Her surmise was proved correct when he picked up her wrap and placed it around her shoulders. 'I can hardly wait for my lessons to begin—let's go, I've ordered dinner for eight.'

This time they journeyed inland. She stole a sideways glance as the car rushed through the half-light of early evening and could not resist a thrill of pride in her escort. Besides the unusual good looks a razor had uncovered, a lighthearted assurance seemed to have taken the place of unbending grimness she had found so quailing. He was actually *humming* as he drove, a lively toe-tapping melody to match a mood which, if continuing indefinitely, promised to play havoc with all her firm intentions. She decided the time was ripe to revise her position in order that she did not become tempted to forget her role of teacher and also to combat an uneasy suspicion that she could be a pupil attempting to instruct a sage.

'The most important thing to remember is that a woman likes to be paid such small courtesies as being helped off with her wrap, for instance, making certain she's seated comfortably and seeing that wherever she's heading doors are held open for her.'

'Eh ... ?' Obviously his mind had been far from the subject in hand. 'Oh, yes, of course! One must remember to open doors, I've got that! Anything else I should know before I'm let loose on civilized society?'

She gave him a quick look, suspecting a hint of dryness, but his expression was serene. 'One or two compliments won't go amiss—everyone is flattered at being told they're looking their best. Admire a girl's dress, her hair-style, her complexion—not her make-up, however,' she added swiftly, envisaging pitfalls. 'Ideally that should have been too well applied to appear other than natural.'

'As yours is,' he murmured, slewing the car to a standstill. His purposeful manner caused alarm bells to jangle in her mind. His arm slid across the back of her seat and the smell of tobacco and cologne mingled beneath her nostrils when he peered down into her apprehensive face.

'Your dimple is as good as a barometer.' His finger slowly traced along the corner of her mouth. 'It appears when you're happy and is absent whenever you're sad . . .' She felt too suffocated to answer, too surprised even to move. 'Fascinating,' he decided, 'but then I find everything about you is fascinating, dear Raine; eyes like deep tarns with captive bluebells in their midst, your elfin face and haunted, sensitive mouth. Are you one of the "little people" sent to confuse me with your fey ways?'

It was she who was confused. Was he sincere? By some happy chance did he feel suddenly attracted or—her blood ran cold—was he simply acting on her advise, practising the exercise set by teacher? Uncertainty overcame wishful thinking; she averted her head and addressed a strangulated sentence to the car window.

'You're progressing very well, keep it up and you'll have no further need to envy Britt.'

A deep throaty laugh was his answer.

She remained squeezed tensely in the corner of her seat until they turned into a drive and drew up in front of what appeared to be a large country house. Light streamed from every window and as a doorman helped her out of the car music spilled from the entrance hall, accompanied by the muted conversation of people seated at tables grouped around a bar. Every eye seemed to swivel towards them as they walked in, but after cursory nods to a few acquaintances Thor directed all his attention upon herself, taking such care with the disposal of her wrap and the positioning of her chair she began to feel perversely and unaccountably annoyed.

'Champagne,' he instructed a hovering wine waiter, before he settled in a chair and turned quizzical eyes in her direction.

'Is it my imagination, or am I right in suspecting that your mood has changed? Don't you like it here, if not, we'll move on somewhere else?'

'How could I possibly find fault with such luxury?' she stammered, stampeded into a swift reply.

'Then why has your dimple disappeared?' he demanded. 'You haven't smiled once since we left the car.'

It was impossible not to respond to this grave badinage. Her lips twitched and the dimple reappeared, accompanied by a blush that emphasized her shy pleasure.

'That's better.' His words turned into a growl halfway. 'Ignore whatever doubts are disturbing you and relax, let this first lesson set the pattern for all those that are to follow!'

After the first sip of champagne she found she was better able to follow his advice. The wine sparkled against her tongue, stroked a deceptive caress along her throat, then raced in wild abandon through her veins. She coughed, and immediately he showed concern.

'Careful! I ought to have warned you to sip slowly. "Over a bottle many a friend is found",' he quipped, 'but at the rate you're drinking the stuff our fictitious marriage could end up a concrete fact!'

The idea was so appealing she felt bound to refute it. 'No, thank you, the man I marry will have to have a greater need of me than that of a bed warmer and a propagator of sons.'

He eyed her keenly. 'Tell me, what are these other needs he'll require?'

She stared across the rim of her glass, wondering at his eagerness to know her innermost secrets, then, deciding he regarded her merely as a sample of a puzzling sex, she told him simply, 'He'll need to love me as much as I love him. Our children will be a part of that love, brought up as happy individuals yet remaining part of a united family. My husband,' she stumbled over the word, 'will need to demonstrate his affection daily, as I will myself, with some small gesture of regard—a posy of flowers, perhaps, a rosy apple polished until it shines, a smile across the breakfast table or a swift cuddle in some handy corner. Such actions keep a marriage alive,' she stated simply. 'I couldn't bear to be part of a meaningless charade, lacking in love, respect or concern. I'd rather die a spinster,' she affirmed, beautiful in her solemnity, 'than marry a man whose own interests are his primary concern.'

'Within my own admittedly limited experience I've found selfishness to be a female rather than a male characteristic,' he protested dryly, lifting a slim-necked bottle from its nest of cracked ice. He topped up her glass, then added, 'But I am prepared to accept that in that respect you could be unique. The man you marry will count himself fortunate in possessing a wife with qualities such as yours. Truthfulness, sincerity, a loving heart and a kind disposition,' he evaluated slowly, placing stress upon each virtue, 'I envy the fellow, in fact, I wish——' He broke off and thankfully Raine surfaced. She was breathless, as emotionally disturbed as if she had been expertly wooed.

She lifted her glass with a shaking hand and sipped slowly, carefully avoiding his eyes. It was a foolish thing to do, because already the wine was having a heady effect, but she badly needed courage to assist her in carrying out her part of an experiment which seemed to be getting totally out of hand. Her brilliant pupil might easily become frustrated with a teacher who succumbed so easily to his planned campaign.

He seemed not to notice her agitation as he escorted her into the dining-room, carrying out his duties as host with an aplomb she found amazing. Without consulting her he made his choice from a menu so imposing she was glad to let him decide.

'Lobster Newburg. No, change that to Lobster Thermidor, the cheese and mustard sauce makes the dish rather outstanding.' When the waiter nodded he continued, 'As Boeuf Bourguignonne is a speciality of the house we might as well have that as our main course—and fetch another bottle of champagne. *La bonne cuisine demand du temps!*' He grinned at Raine. 'So we might as well dance while we are waiting.'

The trio of musicians was playing music chosen especially to suit the ambiance of relaxed luxury. With nerves beating a tattoo of trepidation she slid into his arms, wondering how long she could stand being in such close proximity with the man whose touch she both dreaded and desired. His hand closed upon her waist, drawing her so near she could feel the beat of his powerful heart, and as they slowly circled the floor she felt the brush of his cheek seconds before the suspicion of a kiss landed against her temple.

Caution fled as she melted against him, tempting as a flower to a marauding bee, then after a quickly-indrawn breath his arms tightened with crushing force and his steps slowed until, almost at a stand-still, they swayed together in time to the music, bathed in the shadows of dim lighting, surrounded by couples as engrossed as themselves but aware only of each other and the pulsating force urging them to forget completely the world existing mere steps away.

With a roll of drums the music ended and lights sprang up, startling them apart. Thor's eyelids were slitted over eyes darkly green as he bowed his thanks before leading Raine by the hand with a grip that did not relax until they reached their table. Silently he fumed while the first course was served, then once the waiter had retreated he brought a blush to her cheeks with the compli-ment,

'Those few short minutes made my adolescent attempts to learn how to dance well worth while. Thank you for helping to satisfy an ambition of agonized youth.'

Shyly she smiled. 'It's strange, but for a split sec-ond before we began to dance I wasn't sure whether or not I could. Then when you took me into your arms I knew I could do anything you asked of me—you make me feel so safe...' Her voice wobbled as unexpected tears took her by surprise. 'When I'm with you I feel I could climb mountains or even brave the sea! In time I might even pluck up enough courage to begin unearthing my past, someone, somewhere must know who I am and where I belong!'

'Doctor Kendall insisted that you were not to force yourself to remember,' he reminded her sharply. 'There'll always be a home for you at Danes' Dyke, you know that, so why bother unearthing secrets which alarm or distress you? Don't deny that they do!' he insisted when she made to interrupt, 'too many times I've sensed in you a terror best left undisturbed. You're happy now, and could be even happier in the future, so why try to retrace steps back into an unhappy past?'

She toyed with the food on her plate, wishing she had not allowed discord to spoil what had promised to be an exceptional evening. But now that the subject had been broached she felt she had to explain the doubts that were tormenting her. 'I feel I owe it to you to make some effort to dispel my anonymity. Only the other day,' she gulped, 'Janice, quite unthinkingly, sowed a seed of doubt by asking about the Irish troubles and on which side my sympathies lay. Although I fobbed her off without committing myself, I became suddenly conscious of the fact that I could be deeply involved—might even be wanted for some criminal offence, and if that should prove to be the case and Janice and

Britt were ever to find out they would have a perfect weapon with which to fight for the custody of their son.'

Far from being shocked Thor seemed to find the theory amusing. For the first time since she had begun her explanation a grin split his face, creasing his cheeks into lovable laughter lines. With difficulty he controlled his twitching lips and strove for a solemnity to match the worry shadowing her young face.

'I'm sorry,' he assured her gravely, 'but I simply can't equate you with a gun-toting terrorist on the run. Basically you're far too timid; your gentle heart would never allow you to destroy because you are one of life's builders, not one of its despoilers. Believe me, child, such thoughts can be banished from your mind, I could far easier imagine Vulcan with a price upon his head!'

Encouraged by her tentative smile he lifted his glass, inviting her to join him in a toast. 'To a successful evening,' his eyebrow quirked, 'and to the eventual passing of my exams!'

For the rest of the evening he allowed her no time for retrospective thought. They danced a little, ate a little, drank a little, and all the time Thor concentrated on his lessons, flattering, complimenting, caressing with words and glances until her head was spinning with happiness even though her heart was weighed down with nagging doubt. She managed not to show that each compliment was a two-edged sword inflicting both agony and ecstasy. It was happiness enough to see him completely at ease, acting as a young man should and not bowed down by a weight of responsibility. Her inward glow owed as much to the knowledge that she was being of use to him as it did to the warmth in green eyes that could not seem to stray from her flushed, animated face, and to words that plucked music from her heartstrings—whispered, teasing words she had to argue with herself were not sincere.

The evening reached a climax of bliss as they swayed together to the strains of the last waltz. She felt beautifully drowsy, cradled in arms reluctant to let her go. He held her close and continued humming the melody in her ear until long after the floor was deserted and the sympathetically grinning musicians had packed up and left for home. Warm and deeply content, she burrowed her head deeper into his shoulder and reacted with a gurgle of laughter when he lifted her from her feet and began carrying her out to the car.

The drive home passed in a sleepy blur until a cold draught blasting its way through her flimsy wrap jerked her awake and she saw the steps of Danes' Dyke and Thor in the act of leaning forward to lift her from the car.

'I can manage,' she mumbled sleepily, but was firmly pinioned when she began to struggle.

'Relax, infant,' he growled, rubbing his cheek against her hair as he swept through the hall and into the drawing-room where a fire was crackling a welcome from the grate. 'Stay there,' he deposited her on the sofa and laughed softly when she promptly snuggled deep, 'I'll make a pot of coffee.'

In a surprisingly short time he returned. Raine

sensed him leaning over her, then heard his deep-throated chuckle. Rendered wanton by warmth and comfort, she kept her eyes closed and tilted her mouth, inviting his kiss. Quickly he accepted the invitation, his lips inflicting sadistic, cruel demands on her mouth, throat and the curve of her shoulders. The shock was so great she was incapable of physical resistance; unwilling to reject completely the lips that earlier had coaxed whereas now they branded. She choked out a loving protest, and at the same time reached out to delay the fiery head bent upon sampling to the full the pleasures she had so foolishly offered.

'Darling. . . !' she protested.

As her whisper reached the man watching from the doorway he flinched. 'Must you covet *everything* I possess, Britt?'

The bitter question burned its way into her brain. It was Thor's voice, a furiously angry Thor, directing words from *somewhere behind her*!

Incredible doubt became fact when the man bending over her shrugged himself erect to face his accuser.

'Well, she did encourage me, old man, and as you well know, I've never been able to refuse a lady!'

CHAPTER TWELVE

BRITT had disappeared. With the ease of a man much used to similar situations he had sauntered out of the room leaving behind an atmosphere fraught with unvoiced accusations. Too startled to move, Raine remained pressed into the nest of cushions watching Thor advancing towards her, his eyes glittering a warning of anger about to erupt.

'Thor, I mistook Britt for you, I had no idea——'

'That I would reappear so suddenly,' he grated, 'otherwise you would have postponed your flirtation until a more opportune time!' He halted, jaw-muscles working as he fought to control white-hot fury and a resentment so violent his whole body seemed tensed to spring. 'How long has this been going on?' he spat savagely. 'How many other times has brother Britt enjoyed your favours while my back was turned? God, what a fool I've been!' His hard laughter stabbed her heart. 'Britt's philosophy has always been that a man may have whatever he can take and keep whatever he can hold and by heaven this thinking is not far wrong! I've listened to you preach a gospel of kindness and love, I've even been stupid enough to spend an entire evening practising methods which I now know are based upon lies and misconception. The truth is that women *want* to be taken, *need* to be held!'

Her shocked eyes widened when he swooped

down to menace with a quietness that was terrifying. 'I shall have no further need of your tuition because in future I intend to adopt my brother's tried and proven methods, but as I shall still need a female on which to practise you can be of use to me by providing me with the opportunities of discovering all I need to know about prevarication, deceit and that most confusing of all female characteristics—the compulsion to say no when what is actually meant is yes!'

Raine closed her eyes long before the verbal thrashing ceased. No explanation could have penetrated his jealous rage, so she had no choice but to remain silent, flinching from the insults she felt could be excused because of his deep sense of betrayal. She longed for him to go, to leave her alone to shed tears of regret for the death of the beautiful understanding that had made their evening unforgettable. Now that carefully woven tapestry of trust had been ripped apart by one man's conceit aided by another's inability to recognise his own attraction.

But one protest had to be made. Through a throat tight with tears she forced out the plea, 'There's nothing between myself and Britt, *nothing*; I was drowsy ... thinking of our wonderful evening, wishing it didn't have to end ...'

'But it hasn't ended—yet.' The grim tone was full of intent.

Her wondering eyes fastened upon his face, searching for some sign of softening, but finding none. Implacably he stared back, daring her to profess herself puzzled by his terse statement, ready to combat any protest with cutting words. A blush rose in her cheeks as he began examining her with clinical detachment. With eyes lingering upon the rapid fall and rise of her breast beneath a cloud of golden chiffon he proffered the insulting compliment.

'You have quite a good figure—petite, but pleasing.' Large hands reached out to span her slender waist and his tight lips stretched into a caricature of a smile when he felt her shudder. 'How easily such delicate bones would break under pressure!' His grip tightened unbearably. 'Don't fight me, Raine, relax, and if it will help at all try pretending it's Britt who's about to kiss you.'

Her attempt to escape was crushed to extinction by arms that trapped her against a chest of steel. As her head fell back his lips descended to stroke a kiss along the tender column of her neck, then remained hovering around the hollow of her throat, ruthlessly tormenting. A sob was the only response he allowed before storming her mouth with hot, demanding kisses that jolted her numbed senses into an ecstatic furore, first drawing warmth, then flame, from her icy lips. 'Please don't ... !' she gasped when momentarily she evaded him, then was swamped by a tide of longing when her lips were immediately recaptured to suffer further passionate punishment.

Her own traitorous response was her greatest humiliation; her greatest degradation Thor's complete mastery over his emotions. Thoroughly, competently, he reduced her to clay willing to be moulded by him into any shape he desired. She despised but could not fight an urge to respond, betraying not a whimper when his giant hands crushed, yet when his lips grew tender and stroked across her bruised mouth muttering a smothered curse her sigh of forgiveness caused him a groan of shame.

'Why did you deceive me?' he gasped against her smooth cap of hair. 'Why *Britt*?'

Immediately she attempted to reassure him, but was baulked by bitter condemnation blazing from eyes intensely green. 'All women are cheats, they make a virtue out of lying and get a vicarious thrill out of deceiving gullible men! My father was right: "Use women as they would use you," he often said, "and give not one of them the opportunity of making you look a fool".'

Enraged anew by the reminder, he swept her roughly into his arms and strode out of the room. Her feather-light resistance made no impact upon him as he ascended the stairs and headed swiftly towards her room. She could have cried out, but the thought of disturbing Vulcan who was sleeping nearby made her hesitate until it was too late. Thor entered her room and closed the door behind him with a savage kick, then in two strides he reached the bed where his grasp slackened and she landed among the covers in a confused, apprehensive heap.

'Have you gone completely out of your mind?' she choked, mindful of alert ears.

'I *was* a little mad,' he agreed, 'mad enough to believe you different from the rest of your sex, mad enough even to think you incapable of lying, but

I assure you I'm now completely sane.'

Deliberately he slipped out of his jacket and began loosening his tie. Grappling with the fear knotting her vocal chords, Raine questioned hoarsely, 'What do you mean to do?'

The quirk of his eyebrow was intimidating. 'I should have thought my purpose obvious. You aren't averse to bestowing favours upon Britt, to whom you owe nothing, whereas, by your own admission, you are indebted to me for the roof over your head and the clothes on your back. Does it not follow that I'm entitled to consider a night in your company fair recompense?'

Bitterness had indeed scored deeply into the soul of the man who seemed to be deriving much satisfaction from her shocked distress. From the centre of the bed Raine stared at him, a frightened waif, youthfully unsure of how best to handle the angry man in whose veins ran the blood of lusty, plundering Vikings whose determination to revenge a wrong knew no bounds. To argue had proved useless, an appeal to his chivalrous instincts would be brushed aside with scorn, there was only one option left—a plea for mercy.

She scrambled from the bed and ran to kneel at his feet. Ignoring the derisive curl of his lips, she fastened troubled eyes upon his grim features and pleaded, 'You don't mean that, Thor, neither do you believe those dreadful accusations to be true. Once, in a moment of stress, I accused you of seeking payment and you were insulted, yet now you're asking me to accept that your actions this evening are motivated by a belief that I'm in your debt. I owe you a lot, much more than I can ever hope to repay, and believe me, if what you're asking of me were sufficient I would willingly pay. But it isn't! Under such circumstances you would end up despising yourself for allowing anger to undermine your judgement! We were so happy this evening, yet you allowed jealousy of Britt to ruin what could have been perfect. Please don't make the same mistake twice. What could you possibly hope to gain from an hour of love that would have to be paid for by a lifetime of hatred?'

For a precarious moment she thought she had won. Thor seemed to hesitate, the brilliant green glance softening a little as it dwelt upon her troubled face, but then, as if prodded by some devil that would give him no respite, his profile hardened and both his look and his voice grew chill. 'What do I hope to gain?' he derided. 'You underestimate yourself, gentle Raine!'

Roughly she was pulled to her feet and marched across to the mirror. 'Look there!' He grasped a handful of black hair and twisted her head round so that she was faced with her own frightened image. 'Find your answer in what you see!'

A pale cameo face stared back at her, a youthful face childishly contoured, with mouth still quivering and wide blue eyes fringed by thick silken lashes beating an agitated flutter against cheeks afire with confusion. Behind her, his strong Viking face loomed, each feature outlined by a satanic brush, his mouth a bitter stroke, his angry eyes glinting a desire for revenge.

'You're a desirable wench,' his image assured

hers through the glass. 'When first I was forced to accept you into my home I was resentful. For years I had endured a celibate existence, endurable only because lack of female company had meant lack of temptation. But from the very beginning I knew you could wreck havoc in my life, even unkempt hair and disreputable clothes couldn't detract from tantalizing curves and a grace of movement I found distracting. That's why I fought against having you here, why subconsciously I refused even to admit your need of proper clothes and the usual fripperies necessary to a woman's well being. I wanted you kept in the background, to infringe as little as possible on my mind—but, damn you, you began to encroach exactly as I knew you would, exercising your wiles on Vulcan's behalf, every day making me more acutely aware of my masculine needs yet at the same time making obvious your aversion to my rough and ready ways.'

He moved closer, supporting her drooping head on his shoulder. There was no pity in his smile for the girl who stood rigid as a statue while he listed her faults, then remained silent, awaiting further condemnation from the man who seemed to have wiped from his mind completely the pleasures they had shared and seemed determined to dwell only upon the irritations.

His head lowered and a stray beam from an overhead lamp caught the movement, turning his hair into a fiery beacon. 'My first mistake was in allowing you to infiltrate into my home.' He iced against her ear. 'My second was in believing you different from the other women who brought unhappiness to

Danes' Dyke. But the third mistake,' he tightened his grip, 'was *yours* in over-estimating the extent to which I could be fooled!'

Unbearably tormented, Raine tore out of his grasp and stumbled across the width of the room. 'Stay where you are!' she panted, when he moved towards her. 'I can't bear you to touch me!'

He whitened, his limbs taking on the stillness of stone. But she was too overwrought to care, he was bent upon destroying the only delicate thing of beauty she possessed—her love for him—and every instinct urged her to fight his thirst for revenge with the only weapons she had left—contempt and scorn.

'You're a hypocrite, Thor! You profess to despise me, yet the one you really despise is yourself because of the resentment you feel for your brother. Britt has had everything you've ever wanted—a wife, a son, a career—even your father's love—and all at the lift of a finger, whereas you who have tried so hard have stood in the background feeling more and more conscious of rejection. Janice was right to point out to you the futility of trying to copy your brother!'

She hated to see him flinch, but the point had to be made. However, remorse disrupted her bravado, so that when she continued her words sounded more like a plea. 'Such action is so unnecessary, Thor. Why don't you cast off your brother's shadow and reveal your true self—basically, you're a much nicer person than he could ever be ...'

The room was a tomb of silence. Appalled by her daring, Raine turned her back on the immobile figure and began toying nervously with a three-pronged iron hook set incongruously upon the wall. 'How typical of Halden men,' she fretted, 'to consider a whaling hook a fitting adornment for a bedroom!' But then whaling men were noted more for toughness and strength than for finesse, yet once their hooks were thrown they were impossible to dislodge...

'Would you be willing to marry me?' The savage question seemed torn from him against his will. She jerked so suddenly one of the pointed spikes punctured her finger. She spun round, clenching her fist to hide a spurt of blood, and levelled an incredulous look across the intervening space.

'What ... what did you say?'

'I think you heard.' He waited, standing as he must often have stood on the bridge, stiffly erect, supporting a weight of reponsibility on his solitary shoulders.

His change of attitude was so surprising she experienced a stab of hope. 'Why?' was all she dared breathe.

White linen stretched taut across massive shoulders when he shrugged, moving forward so that light illuminated his cynical features. 'I need a wife, but as this evening's experience has underlined my inability to discriminate between feminine sincerity and feminine deceit I'm willing to settle for a woman whose weaknesses are known to me rather than fall foul of one whose failings might be even greater. Also Vulcan needs a mother and you need a home. Can you think of three better reasons?'

Her soaring heart descended with a thud.

'You make no mention of love . . .'

'I've lived all my life without love,' he returned bleakly. 'But if you find such an emotion necessary, I'm sure Vulcan could supply you with an outlet for your maternal instincts as well as gaining you the satisfaction of ensuring that under your guidance he will develop along different lines from those of his uncle.'

His wish to safeguard the child to whom he had sacrificed part of his life touched a sympathetic chord. He could offer her nothing of himself, yet he was willing to trust her with his most precious charge. 'You offer marriage, yet you make no secret of your contempt. You imply that you will expect nothing more of me than to be a companion for Vulcan—yet how can I believe you,' she queried softly, 'when you've already admitted and indeed demonstrated your needs?'

He flushed a dull red. 'You need have no worries on that score,' he replied harshly. 'If you should decide to accept my offer of marriage I promise never to encroach any further than you would wish.'

She remembered the delight of being held in his arms, the excitement of his caresses, the sheer ecstasy of his kisses, and wondered if she dared accept his proposal knowing how much she was likely to suffer. But he needed her—though he would die rather than admit it—even more so than Vulcan whose childish dependence would have to suffice in place of the rugged tenderness for which she yearned.

'Very well.' Tense fingers pleated the fine material of her skirt as nervously she lied, 'For Vulcan's sake, I'll marry you.'

Tension drained out of him at the whispered words. For a second she could have suspected her acceptance could not have meant more to him had he been an uncertain lover waiting eagerly to learn his fate. But the supposition was squashed by the cruel reply.

'I didn't doubt you would. I'll see about a special licence in the morning—later this morning,' he corrected, scanning his watch. 'The act should be accomplished in a matter of days.'

Raine stared as the door closed behind him. With the masterful tread of a mariner he had gone, leaving her to wrestle with the doubts and fears crowding her mind. Slowly she sank upon the bed to digest the incredible fact that she had just promised to marry a man who did not want her. A sob caught in her throat. The austerity of his proposal had been bad enough, but only now was she beginning to appreciate all she was about to miss: an exciting courtship, the support of loving parents, announcements in the press, the choosing of a wedding dress, the sending out of invitations—the list of things dear to a young bride's heart was endless and in her case totally unattainable.

Dry-eyed, she stared up at the ceiling, telling herself that although it was best to love wisely, to love foolishly need not be totally disastrous. Her heart began to pound as she unearthed Thor's words. *The act should be accomplished in a matter of days!* How curt he had sounded, how sternly his lips had settled around the words. Yet earlier this evening he had proved himself capable of warmth, gentleness, even mild teasing, and before Britt's intervention his manner had promised very much more . . .

Agitation subsided as she recalled those moments of perfect rapport. He had bound himself with a promise never to encroach, but with the qualification: *'any further than you would wish!'*

A smile touched lips curving with optimism. Thor's forceful masculinity rendered him so vulnerable, perhaps in time he would weaken and allow her love to lead him forward into a life of happiness.

CHAPTER THIRTEEN

'THOR,' Janice informed Raine next morning,
'breakfasted early and by now is probably halfway
to York. He seemed more than usually tense,' she
offered, her sharp eyes noting purple smudges beneath Raine's eyes. 'Did you two have a fight last
night?' She continued to butter a piece of toast,
watching covertly for Raine's reaction.

Carefully Raine set down her cup and buried
shaking hands in her lap, but an unfortunate tide
of colour was less easy to control. 'Of course not,'
she mumbled, knowing Janice was not fooled, 'he
was probably feeling a bit put out, as you know, he
spends as little time as possible in town, but urgent
business made this visit to York imperative.'

Janice grimaced. 'York is hardly the centre of the
universe, but it's certainly preferable to this deadly
hole. God, how I hate this place!' Irritably she
pushed aside her plate and reached for a cigarette.
'I told Britt last night,' she puffed savagely, 'that a
week of this place is six days more than I can stand.
He insists, however, that we must remain here until we've won over that wretched boy.' She returned Raine's shocked look with a hard laugh.
'Ironic, isn't it? Initially I was the one who wanted
to resume parental duties, but now Britt is determined to fight to the bitter end for what he
claims are his rights. But that's typical of Britt,' she

screwed the butt of her cigarette into an ashtray with such intensity Raine winced. 'Tell him there's something he can't have and he'll fight all the way to hell to get it—especially,' she added wryly, 'if that something belongs to Thor! One always imagines twins as being compatible, each eager for the well-being of the other, but that's never been the case with Britt. I'm not blameless myself, but when I ran away I considered it was in the child's best interests to leave him here, whereas Britt, I feel sure, was more interested in curtailing Thor's career!'

Raine was appalled. Something about Janice's discontented expression, about the way her fingers were drumming an irritable tattoo on the table top, seemed to indicate that she was in no mood to care that temper was being allowed to overrule discretion. Yet her suggestion was so incredible she felt bound to protest, 'Surely not! What satisfaction could Britt hope to gain?'

'The satisfaction of knowing a competitor had been removed from his orbit, my dear! Thor was becoming too much talked about, too brilliantly successful in his career, and in this family only Britt has ever been allowed to shine.'

Raine looked away from Janice's contorted features. 'How can you suspect such a thing of the man you profess to love?' she rebuked quietly.

Reverting to calmness, Janice reached for a second cigarette. 'Love is for fools,' she directed a stream of smoke through arrogantly distended nostrils, 'we understand one another, Britt and I, far better than some couples who profess to have the perfect marriage. We're both selfish, both like luxury and enjoy living well, and we're neither of us hesitant to do whatever is necessary to gain our ends.'

'And what about Vulcan?' Raine almost choked in her indignation. 'If you were to succeed in prising him away from Thor how would he fit into your plans?'

Janice's glance sharpened. 'We'll worry about that when the time comes—which reminds me,' she heaved out of her chair, 'I'd better start work bringing the little devil round; a protracted stay in this house will drive me out of my mind!'

Raine watched helplessly as she sauntered out in search of Vulcan, the son she spoke of with such lack of affection it was hard to accept her claim to motherhood. Doubtless, if ever the pair managed to regain custody of their son he would, once the novelty had worn off, be dumped in some boarding school and left to pine his heart out for his beloved Luci, for his home and for his Uncle Thor. The idea was so unbearable her heart lurched and recovered only slightly at the reminder that Thor was even now in the process of ensuring such a possibility became remote. A loveless marriage, weighed against a child's deep unhappiness, was a much more bearable alternative...

She spent the rest of the morning indoors, tormented by sounds of childish laughter coming from an unsuspecting Vulcan being wooed by an enjoyable game of cricket.

'Well held, son!' Raine flinched from Britt's blatant misuse of the parental address. 'Now let's see if you can bowl Mummy out!'

She wandered up to her room and closed the windows against the sounds of treachery, made shiveringly aware of Thor's absence by the chill penetrating her bones, the creeping fear that only his presence kept at bay.

Lunch had to be faced, however, and it was with great reluctance that she made her way downstairs to the dining-room just as the ancient grandfather clock in the hall struck the hour of one. It had a rich, resonant tone reminiscent of Thor, so she gave it an affectionate pat on her way past, grateful for its timely encouragement. She heard voices coming from the drawing-room, Vulcan, Britt and Janice were discussing some subject obviously absorbing enough to delay lunch. She veered towards the half open door and was almost on the threshold when she heard Vulcan's piping voice incautiously informing them,

'That's the diary Uncle Thor started to help Raine find her memory. We used to write lots of things in it, but nobody's bothered much lately.'

Stiff with shock, Raine remained poised outside the door hoping the boy's lapse would pass unnoticed. It was a vain hope.

'So Raine has lost her memory! That explains quite a lot,' Janice murmured, smooth as cream. 'Tell me, did the loss occur before or after her arrival here?'

'Before.' Raine closed her eyes as Vulcan prattled on, happily unaware of the fact that his future happiness was at stake. 'At first, Simeon said she was a tramp looking for an easy place to lay her head—even Thor didn't believe her until Doctor Randall said he must let her stay. But everyone believes her now,' he confided happily, 'we all love her, even though we've only known her a few——'

He stopped so abruptly that even without seeing him Raine sensed realization had struck. She suffered with him the sense of betrayal he must have been feeling, but could not condemn even for a moment the childish naïveté that had made the disclosure possible.

'Yes, go on,' Britt insisted. 'A few *weeks*, were you about to say?'

'No, n ... no!' Vulcan stumbled desperately, 'Raine's lived here for years and years ...'

'Little liar!' Janice rapped. 'The truth is, she'd been here no more than a few weeks and the tale Thor spun about their being married simply isn't true! Am I right? Tell me, you wicked boy!'

Raine could bear it no longer. Gathering up her courage, she drew in a deep breath and stepped inside the room. Janice and Britt were threatening the cowering child whose riotous red hair was clashing starkly against his ashen, frightened face. Relief flared like a beacon when he saw her appear like an avenging angel to rescue him from his tormentors. Joyfully he ran to her, throwing his arms around her waist and burying his head deep in the folds of her skirt.

'I'm sorry, Raine, I'm sorry,' she heard him sob.

'It doesn't matter, darling,' she consoled, hugging him tight. 'It wasn't your fault.'

'No, indeed.' Britt sounded sarcastically amused. 'Whose idea was it to masquerade as man and wife, not yours, I bet, yet the blame lies uneasily on the shoulders of my puritanical brother?'

'We were equally to blame,' Raine admitted with dignity, 'and we'd do the same thing again if it meant keeping the boy out of your clutches.'

'No chance!' Britt laughed exultantly. 'The boy leaves with us, just as soon as we can complete our packing. Ask yourself,' he gloated, 'what would be the reaction of any magistrate called upon to judge our case? However broadminded, he wouldn't dare give custody of the child to a couple who are, to put it crudely, living in sin!'

'We are not!' In her agitation Raine relaxed her grip on Vulcan as she stepped forward to stress. 'Thor, at this very moment, is making arrangements for us to be married by special licence, so we'll be man and wife within a very few days.'

Britt's lips parted to reply, but Janice forestalled him with a drawl that was sibilant and deadly. 'But, my dear, wouldn't that be rather unwise? After all, if you really are suffering a loss of memory how can you be certain you're not already married?'

Raine stared up at the patch of damp on her bedroom ceiling. For hours she had lain motionless on her bed trying to overcome the effects of words that had dealt her a body blow. Janice's question hammered on the door of her mind. *Was* she married? Useless to argue that the answer was no simply because she wore no ring. Rings were easy to obtain and just as easy to discard. She groped for the rings Thor insisted she wore always, taking comfort from an inner sense that assured her they had a right to be there. But such assurance was not enough, she had to be *certain* before committing herself and Thor to a marriage that might turn out to be illegal!

Restlessly she swung her feet to the floor. Shadows were gathering behind heavy furniture and in the cavernous corners of her room, so Vulcan's suppertime must be imminent. She stole a glance out of the window and saw that storm clouds were marshalling over the moors and beneath them sheep were flocking together, bleating their nervous fear of elements they sensed were preparing to erupt. *'Thor, why don't you come!'* she pleaded in a whisper, tracing with worried eyes the grey ribbon of road. She could not bear his absence, without his broad-shouldered support she felt adrift, rudderless, stormed by worry. She loved him desperately, needed his warmth, his rugged strength and confidence. She also needed his *love*, but would somehow have to survive on bare approval.

Shaking off a sense of foreboding, she walked down the passageway to Vulcan's room. A glance around satisfied her that he was not inside, but as she was about to close the door some instinct impelled her to examine more closely the deserted room. A wardrobe door fell open at her touch, revealing more than usual disarray. Half-open drawers held underwear tossed into untidy heaps, as if hastily rifling hands had selected certain essential items, then rejected the rest.

Panic reared inside her. Fighting a desire to scream, she ran out of the room, down the stairs, then out through the kitchen, making towards the stables. Simeon glanced up, startled, as she flew past him, then threw down his knife and followed her. She was leaning against Luci's empty stall when he caught her up. Utter dejection bowed her slim body as she turned to him with eyes dark with remorse. 'He's gone,' she choked, 'Vulcan's gone and he's taken Luci with him! Oh, why didn't I realize how upset he must have been...! I was so taken up with my own troubles I forgot he'd heard Britt threatening to take him away...'

Simeon was swift to react. 'Don't you fret, Miss Raine, we'll soon find him! I'll call the men together and form a search party, knowing Vulcan, he'll be heading towards the coast, he's seldom been inland and what friends he has are scattered round about the harbour.'

'Of course!' she grasped eagerly at the straw of hope, 'he's bound to be heading in that direction!' Galvanised into action, she heaved down a saddle from the wall and stumbled into the adjoining stall. 'Inform Britt straight away, ask him to drive inland while you and the others search in the opposite direction! I'll travel across country on horseback—between us we're sure to find him!'

'But, Miss Raine, there's no need for you to take part, there's a storm brewing and being a stranger to these moors you're almost certain to lose your way.'

'Don't stand there arguing!' she snapped with such authority he automatically backed away. She was saddling up with frantic haste and as soon as the last girth had been tightened she led a startled mare outside and vaulted into the saddle.

'At least wait until I get you a coat!' Simeon yelled after her as she cantered out of the yard, but his only answer was a wildly waving arm, gesturing him to hurry.

As she galloped across the moors she called out Vulcan's name. There was barely half an hour of daylight left, already visibility was so bad that Danes' Dyke was no longer visible on the skyline and sheep were huddling together like grey ghosts, their startled bleating rising with sinister clarity upon the empty air. Anxiously, she scanned the bleak landscape, digging her heels into the mare's flanks each time she spotted movement on the horizon, only to glare bitter disappointment at innocently grazing sheep when she arrived there. Half a dozen times she was so tantalized, each time riding off in a different direction, Vulcan's name rasping from her throat, tormented by the knowledge that the boy's fear must be as quickly mounting as her own.

When rain began to fall, splashing spots large as coins upon her cotton blouse, she thought, for the first time, of taking her bearings. With panic-stricken eyes she searched for some familiar landmark that might guide her back to the road that slashed its way through the cold, rain-driven moorland, but all she could see were towering pylons set amidst miles of scrub—scornful fingers poking derision at the glowering sky, scoffing to the elements: *Do what you will to this tough, indestructible land!*

Thunder roared. Lightning spat, venting its brilliance upon a stone-built shepherd's hut in the distance, and with a gasp of thankfulness Raine spurred on the mare in its direction. As if resenting her escape, the rain increased in volume so that she was riding blindly through a sheet of water that lashed solid force against her slender body. She was bent double in the saddle by the time she reached her goal and slid exhausted to the ground. Praying the hut would not be locked, she thumbed the latch and stumbled inside when the door swung open.

'*Raine!*' The whimper was an answer from heaven.

'Vulcan! Darling ... !' A cowering bundle rose from a dark corner and hurtled into arms that grasped and refused to let go. Not that he wanted them to—Vulcan the brave, the prematurely mature, was frightened half out of his wits!

'Don't let them take me away,' he sobbed against her waist. 'I don't want to leave Luci and Danes' Dyke an' Uncle Thor and you. Please, Raine, please ... !'

'*And you!*' With uplifted heart she savoured the words, admittedly tagged on to the tail end of a list of precious possessions but unexpectedly heartening. Even in the midst of distress she found time to rejoice that one at least of the Vikings of Danes' Dyke had admitted his need of her.

She knelt to gather the sobbing child against her breast, running her fingers through his mop of fiery hair while she assured him fiercely, 'We'll never let you go, darling, I swear it! How could you even think such a thing, your uncle would never allow it?'

His small frame stiffened and sobbing subsided to choked gasps while he considered her words. 'But ... I *belong* to them! Mummy,' he stumbled over the word, 'said that if I didn't do as she said Uncle Thor would be taken to jail. That's why I ran away, I thought that if they couldn't find me they might go away and they wouldn't be able to blame Uncle Thor 'cos he wouldn't know where I was either. I don't want him to be locked up!' his voice rose hysterically high, 'but I'd rather die than go with them!'

'Hush...' Anger churned inside of her as she rocked the unhappy child. For an age she comforted him with hugs and poured out assurances that whatever happened he would not be deprived either of his home or his uncle, and by the time sobs had ceased to rack his small frame the inside of the hut was pitch black and the sodden clothes sheathing her limbs felt icily clammy.

Luckily, Vulcan had taken refuge before the storm had begun so he was completely dry, but when an uncontrollable shiver jerked her limbs she urged through chattering teeth. 'Let's search the hut for kindling, we may be marooned here for hours, so if possible we must try to light a fire.'

With the resilience of the young, Vulcan's spirits recovered. 'I saw a candle earlier, and paper and sticks set in the grate, so all we need are some matches.' Her shivering worsened as blindly they groped for the tiny items that had assumed to her the value of gold. Her stiff fingers could barely feel the outlines of a rough wooden chair placed in the centre of the hut, but a creeping numbness warned her to keep on the move so as to overcome an almost irresistible urge to give in to the lethargy that was weighting her limbs.

'I've found them!' Vulcan's triumphant cry caused her a sob of relief. Raine thrust out her hand and in her eagerness dropped the precious box when he handed it over. Suppressing a cry of distress she dropped to her knees, scrabbling frantically on the floor and when, mercifully, her hand closed around the box she slowly and painfully extracted a match, scratched it along the igniting surface and felt enormously comforted by the resulting flame.

'Quickly, Raine, you'll burn your fingers!' Vulcan's warning shocked her into action. Carefully eager, she thrust match to paper and held her breath as flame licked a curling edge, ignited, then began devouring the kindling in the grate. 'Now the candle!' Vulcan thrust it into the flame and when the wick flared carried it carefully across to the chair.

'Raine, your clothes are soaking.' In the flickering candlelight Vulcan's wide eyes assessed her bedraggled state. Her thin blouse was plastering her body like a second skin and from the hem of her skirt water was dripping into a pool around feet shod only in flat-soled sandals held on by thin straps.

She mustered a smile. 'Don't worry about me, I'll soon dry out,' she assured him as cheerfully as she could, but even to her own ears her voice sounded far distant. To allay his anxiety she urged, 'Look into that cupboard, you may find us something to eat.'

There was a solitary can of soup, but no opener. After half an hour of abortive bashing and prising the can remained defiantly inviolate and lay mocking them from the floor where it had eventually been thrown in disgust. Controlling a surge of vexed tears, she consoled Vulcan, 'Never mind, dear, someone's sure to find us soon. Meanwhile, let's sleep the storm out, when we awake it will be morning and even if no one has come by then we'll be able to make our own way back home.'

On a rough blanket smelling of sheep, they stretched out on the floor in front of the fire, Raine's body sheltering the boy from draughts that were whistling under the badly fitting door. Occasionally, during the night, she manoeuvred an arm around the sleeping child so as to feed the fire with logs from a pile at the side of the fireplace. But in time the effort became too great. Hammers began pounding in her brain, icy numbness disappeared and was replaced by a heat that set her whole body afire. But worst of all were the fantasies that began spinning through her head, frightening, violent scenes in which she seemed to play a major part. She heard the sound of heavy footsteps, men shouting, then felt a hand grasping her head.

Suddenly everything became clear. She screamed, a long, loud echo of despair and lifted up her hands for protection, but before the expected blow could land a curtain of darkness descended and she escaped gladly into a pit of oblivion.

CHAPTER FOURTEEN

SEVERAL times Raine fought her way to the edge of the pit, only to slide, weak and spent, back into unconsciousness. An urgent voice racked with concern commanded her time after time to return, allowing her no peace until she renewed her feeble efforts to fight a selfish desire never to open her eyes again. She had no wish to resume a life of painful problems, the pit of darkness was preferable to the deep unhappiness she sensed a return to light would bring. But the voice left her no choice, continuously it harassed, cajoled and pleaded, determinedly transmitting through waves of darkness a message so urgent it became imprinted upon her subconscious mind. Out there someone needed her, needed her so badly that his once resonant voice had become reduced to a hoarse, agonized croak.

So she gathered her strength for one final effort and managed to reach the rim. Light almost blinded her as she forced heavy lashes apart to search out the owner of the voice to console him with a triumphant grin. Startled green eyes stared at her out of a haggard face made frightening by a stubble of red beard. Fiery hair run through by frantic fingers spiked wildly about his head, and a tight, punished mouth that had forgotten how to smile parted to emit a long, shuddering sigh when her lips slowly framed a caricature of a smile.

Once reclaimed, her recovery was sure. During the following days she became conscious of a nurse ministering to her needs, wiping a damp cloth across feverish cheeks and hands, easing her aching limbs into fresh nightclothes, then gradually introducing a bland diet, sips of nourishing soup, coddled eggs, fish and later even small spoonsful of blancmange.

Visitors were not allowed. Even a brave attempt to converse was discouraged by the nurse who told her firmly to lie quiet and concentrate on regaining her much depleted strength. When the day finally arrived, however, when Raine refused to be silenced, she smiled grudging approval and confirmed, 'Nothing much wrong with you now, my dear. When the doctor calls I'll ask if you can be allowed out of bed for an hour—would you like that?'

'Oh, yes, please,' Raine whispered. 'I'm feeling fine and there's so much I want to know. How long have I been ill? Is Vulcan all right? And when can I speak to Thor?'

'It's just over a week since Doctor Kendall called me in to nurse you,' the nurse smiled, then sobered. 'For the first few days it was doubtful whether or not you would pull through, but thanks to the doctor's skill and Captain Halden's determination, you did.' She uttered a short, admiring laugh. 'The captain *commanded* you to live! Minute by minute, hour by hour, he sat by your bedside urging you to fight, and eventually after three days and nights of ceaseless urging he was rewarded by your response. Doctor Kendall tried to get him to rest—

his eyes were red-rimmed with lack of sleep—but he refused to listen. When we did eventually persuade him he slept the clock round, twenty-four hours non-stop!'

'Poor Thor,' Raine reflected sadly, 'I'm always such a trial to him.'

The nurse looked surprised. 'I wouldn't have said so, my dear, but then I suppose you know best . . .'

She did know, and during the days that followed, while her health gradually improved, she had many hours in which to ponder on the effect she had had upon his life and the relief he would feel when she told him she need no longer be regarded as his responsibility. But for some reason he seemed to be avoiding her. Vulcan had been allowed a short, supervised visit, so obviously her health could not be the reason behind his absence, but when she asked about his non-appearance the replies she received were evasive, as if those questioned were as puzzled as she by his strange behaviour.

Finally she could stand the suspense no longer and when Simeon appeared with a tray of food to tempt her appetite she waved it away with the mutinous statement, 'I refuse to eat another bite until someone has supplied me with some answers! Tell me, are Janice and Britt still determined to take Vulcan away? And what has happened to Thor—he isn't ill, is he?' She caught a pained breath. 'Is that why he hasn't been to see me?'

'Bless you, no!' Simeon shuffled awkwardly.

'He's as right as rain, miss—except for his acting like a bear with a sore head, that is.'

She sank back against her cushions, colour seeping back into her cheeks. 'But Master Britt and his wife left long since,' Simeon continued heartily, hoping to erase her anxious frown. 'There was an almighty bust-up between them when the Skipper arrived back from York and was told you'd gone to search for Vulcan. I don't rightly know the ins and outs of it,' he scratched his head, 'but the Skipper didn't spare a minute in getting a search party organized and we were out best part of the night scouring the moors on horseback, finding our way by torchlight. The Skipper swore,' he grinned, able now to regard with amusement the salty terms in which the words had been broached, 'that he'd flay the skin off any man who returned to Danes' Dyke before you and the boy had been found. And he meant it, too,' he chuckled grimly, 'although he should have known that not one man Jack of us would have come back without you anyway....'

As he paused to reflect upon the unreasonableness of the Skipper's attitude, Raine's delicate fingers clenched and unclenched, urging him to continue. When the silent message eventually penetrated, he carried on, 'It was the Skipper's idea to make for the hut. We tried to dissuade him because it was miles off the beaten track and farther than we guessed you could have reached, but he was adamant—some kind of hunch, a sixth sense, I daresay, must have guided him straight to where you and the boy were stranded. The rest you know,' he concluded, unaware of the gaps he had left unfilled. 'We got you both back to the house as quickly as possible and sent for Doctor Kendall, then shortly after that Master Britt and his wife had a showdown with the Skipper in his study, then packed their bags and left in a hurry. We haven't laid eyes on 'em since,' he grunted with satisfaction, 'nor with luck will we ever again.'

He beamed approval on her small, heart-shaped face, her fragility quickening the beats of a heart that had never before reacted to any woman. He felt shaken by a fervent desire to do anything on earth to please her.

'Simeon,' she husked, her anxious eyes fastened upon his weatherbeaten face, 'will you do something for me? Will you please tell Thor I would like to talk to him and try to persuade him to come immediately . . . or as soon as is convenient?'

'Surely,' he gruffed, then stomped out, struggling to subdue strange, disloyal thoughts regarding the inhumanity of Halden men.

For hours she fretted, tensing at every footfall outside her door, then slumping back into her chair each time the door opened and the man she longed to see did not appear. She was now being allowed to sit part of the day by the window, but was not yet strong enough, the doctor had stressed, to venture out of her room. Because the scattered, isolated community relied so heavily upon its district nurse, he had reluctantly had to ration her services, but even though Raine had protested that she could now manage alone he still insisted upon the nurse visiting her each morning to take her temperature and make her comfortable for the day.

She had departed hours ago and was not due back until tomorrow!

Cautiously Raine eased her way out of the rug tucked around her knees and stood up. She swayed, feeling peculiarly lightheaded, then walked slowly across to the window overlooking the rear of the house. Storm clouds hung low in the air; the moors seemed always to be on the verge of weeping. A group of men were laughing and talking down by the paddock and as she watched a tall red-haired figure strode across to join them. A thrill of pleasure weakened her. Hastily she grabbed at the curtains for support while she hungrily looked her fill of the man whose off-hand treatment had caused her more pain than her illness. Why was he so intent upon avoiding her? A blush scorched her skin as a possibility presented itself—she had been feverish, probably delirious, when he found her—had her tongue rambled recklessly enough to have given her away?

She sagged against the window-frame and closed her eyes, waiting for an agony of humiliation to fade. He had been willing to marry for convenience, but a girl he suspected might be in love with him could turn out to be an embarrassment—so much so that he had decided to keep well out of her way!

She heard his deep-toned voice directing the men, 'Carry on as planned, if anyone wants me I'll be working in my study for the rest of the day.'

A small flame of anger flared. He must have received her message and had obviously decided to ignore it. 'Very well,' she muttered through clenched teeth, 'the mountain must go to Mohammed!'

When she stepped outside her room the chill of the passageway bit through the fine velvet robe that had seemed quite substantial within the room kept beautifully warm by Simeon's constant attention to the fire. She shivered, pulling the collar of her dressing-gown closer around her neck as, wraith-like, she hastened along the corridor and down the stairs. She hesitated outside the study door, weakened by seeping courage, then somewhere, someone opened an outside door and the resulting stream of cold air sent her scurrying to seek the warmth of the inner room.

She had expected to find him working, but when she slipped quietly inside she saw he was leaning heavily against the mantelpiece, his bowed head resting upon an outstretched arm while he moodily kicked at a log smouldering at the edge of the fire. When she made a slight movement his head jerked upwards and at the same time the log spluttered, emitting a flare of light that momentarily illuminated every object in the storm-darkened room. For a second he seemed unable to grasp the identity of the figure poised tensely in the doorway, but when she took a tentative step he sprang forward to draw her farther into the room.

'Raine! For heaven's sake, you should be upstairs...!'

'I have something very important to tell you, Thor. As you haven't answered any of my messages or bothered to come and see me, I decided I must come to you.'

She shivered, and with a muttered curse he propelled her into a chair drawn close to the fire and did not answer until he was satisfied that she was sitting comfortably and was protected from draughts.

'I was delayed,' he told her starkly, 'but given just a few more minutes I would have been on my way up to your room.'

She sent him a pale, wan smile. Judging from his deep absorption his delay had been caused by a need for thought—*of how to get rid of her now that the problem of Britt and Janice no longer existed?*

Words began stumbling from her lips. 'You've been so kind, Thor, I don't know what would have become of me if you hadn't taken me into your home, clothed me, fed me, even considered making me your wife. Of course, we can forget about that now circumstances have changed . . .'

'Have they changed so much?' His voice, grating with harshness, put such a sudden end to her nervous stammering she felt stranded in mid-air, puzzled by the restrained savagery contained within those few terse words. 'Can you truthfully say you haven't always felt towards me the way you feel today?'

He had guessed!

A rush of shamed colour seemed answer enough for the man who, when he saw it, turned his back so that his face was hidden when he continued speaking so quietly she had to strain to hear him. 'There's nothing to be gained from further discussion. You were partly right in what you said, some circumstances *have* changed, Britt and Janice have gone and I have it in writing that they will never again lay claim to the boy, so happily his future, at least, is assured. You need no longer worry,' he stressed harshly, 'that I might try to hold you to your promise to become my wife.'

She ignored his last remark. Her sensitive feelings were bruised by his harsh exposure of her love for him—there must be kinder ways of rejecting unwanted love than resorting to sarcasm. But her anxiety on Vulcan's behalf forced her to question, 'How did you persuade them to leave, they seemed determined never to let Vulcan go?'

Firelight fell upon the grim contours of his face as he bent to manoeuvre a shifting log. 'By offering them the choice of either money or a court action,' he clipped, 'and as the boy had already demonstrated his aversion to them by running away, Britt decided that to accept my offer to buy his half of Danes' Dyke, plus an inducement bonus to leave the boy alone, was more fitting to his dignity. Also, the few choice phrases I threw in on the subject of their suitability as parents might have helped them make up their minds,' he concluded, betraying no sign of emotion.

She gasped, 'That must have cost you quite a lot of money . . .'

'Almost all I had,' he shrugged, 'but that's of little consequence, the money was well spent considering it bought the boy's happiness.'

'If only one could pay to be rid of misery!' she cried silently, nursing inner grief. Her dark head fell against the back of the chair as weariness over-took her. She had not yet managed to inform him of her news, yet the effort to do so was being thwarted by the sensuous heat being thrown by crackling logs and by the blanket of silence that had fallen, isolating them both in an intimacy both pleasurable and painful.

Thor, too, seemed affected. As he watched her heavy lashes wavering upon fire-blushed cheeks his iron profile melted until only concern remained where once anger had been. 'I'm sorry I haven't been to see you sooner,' he apologized softly. 'But I followed your progress very closely; you were ex-tremely brave, little one—when I found you that night I thought at first it was already too late . . .'

Her lashes quivered but did not rise. She could not face meeting the eyes of the man whose voice was registering an emotion she dared not try to name. Then mindful of the debt she owed him, she felt forced to voice her gratitude. 'I believe I owe my life to you.' Their glances met and she veered from the onslaught of green flame. With fast beat-ing heart, Raine decided that now was the time to impart her news, now, when his mood was recep-tive enough to allow her time to explain. 'That night when I almost lost my life, I regained my memory. I know who I am, Thor, and where I be-long, and why I ran away!' The last admission was choked out as wide-eyed with horror she resur-rected the memories that had lain buried in her mind.

'Don't look like that!' Pistol-sharp, Thor pro-tested. Then, seemingly without movement on either part, she was cradled against his hard chest, wrapped around with arms of steel. 'Don't speak of it yet,' he commanded roughly, 'you've endured enough!'

The bliss of feeling him close was ample compensation for any hurt; wrapped around by his strength she felt capable of bearing any agony—except the agony of being denied his love.

'No, I must tell you now,' she pleaded, feeling his muscles tense under her light touch. Her head barely reached his heart, yet she felt in some way dominant when a shudder ran through his mighty frame.

'Then at least sit down,' he rasped, sounding like a man almost at the end of his tether.

Raine wanted to stay within the shelter of his arms, arms that gave her strength when she needed strength, tenderness when she needed tenderness, and courage when her morale was in tatters. But he released her and took a step backwards, putting safe, precise distance between them. Feeling suddenly chilled, she groped her way back to her chair and avoided looking at the erect figure casting a shadow of aloofness over her bent head as she began reliving her nightmare past.

'My home is in Ireland, in a small village on the border dividing north from south. The Troubles didn't intrude much into our lives, we lived very much as we had always done—in a tightly-knit community, caring for neighbours if they were in need, whatever their religious or political beliefs—never dreaming that the horrors being perpetrated in the cities could ever really touch our lives. There were just the two of us,' she whispered, her knuckles showing white, 'my father and myself. Father was a local magistrate, bluff, kindly, but very outspoken in his views on acts of terrorism—too outspoken, as it turned out ...'

The break in her voice reacted upon Thor like a lash. He jerked erect, but checked an impulse to move towards her and remained tensely still while she struggled for control. Bravely gathering up her courage, she continued, 'One night just after supper we were together in the sitting-room listening to the late news when four masked men burst through the door and ordered my father at gunpoint to go outside. I remember screaming at him not to go. My father began to argue and I ran towards the telephone, intending to call the police, but before I could reach it one of the men grabbed me by the hair and threw me to the ground.' A savage hiss from Thor went unheeded as with vague, almost childish pride, she recalled, 'I had long hair reaching almost to my waist, but,' her trembling mouth tautened Thor's clenched jaw, 'they cut it off—to convince my father they meant business, they said, but I think they actually enjoyed inflicting the humiliation.'

For a brief moment her fingers strayed upwards to her gamin head, then halted halfway and descended to her lap. 'Whatever the reason, it worked. My father agreed to do whatever they asked provided they left me alone. When they began dragging him outside I ran after them, screaming, begging them to let him go. Their intention was unmistakable, their eyes glaring cold with hatred, fanaticism and a lust to kill. They shot him right before my eyes,' she faltered, staring blankly in front of her. 'I ran to help him, but even as I dropped to my knees I could see he was dead. Seconds later I felt a blow on the back of my head—I remember nothing more until the time you picked me up on the moors. How I got there I can't remember ...'

'And probably never will!' The frustrated thirst for revenge in Thor's voice caused her a shiver of revulsion.

'I never want to go back!' She could not suppress the broken cry. 'Thor, I need your strength, your protection, please let me stay.... !'

To her utter humiliation he hesitated. It was little consolation to know that he was deeply moved on her behalf, so concerned that every muscle of his tall frame was taut with restrained savagery. He was sorry for her, she sensed, but dared not extend sympathy which she, in her need, might construe as an emotion much stronger.

She swallowed hard, then with great dignity rose to her feet. 'I'm sorry, I had no right to ask you that, I'm over-emotional, not quite myself...' Tears flooded the remainder of her sentence, a rush of misery so shattering she could not continue. Blindly, she spun away hoping to reach the door before the dam burst, but before her first step had been taken he was blocking her way.

'Raine, is your fear so great that you're prepared to spend the rest of your life with a man you hate rather than go back?' Tight-lipped, he warned, 'You've had a dreadful experience, but believe me, child, the memory will fade in time and when it does you'll resent me bitterly for taking advantage of your weak state, because if you stay, Raine, it must be as my wife, there's no other way.'

She stared at his ravaged face, only two of his savagely thrust words registering.

'Hate you...? How could I possibly hate *you*?'

Mustering great effort of will, he chose his words carefully. 'How can you not, when on at least two occasions you've pleaded with me not to touch you? I admit that on the first occasion your fear was justified, but when I broke into the hut where you and Vulcan were sheltering you cowered away as if the sight of me brought you nothing but terror.' With jawline jutting granite hard, he admitted with difficulty, 'Much as Vulcan and I need you, I can't trust myself far enough to renew my earlier promise. I love you far too much to live with you and remain celibate.'

His meaning was unmistakable, but though she blushed wildly her eyes remained steady, registering deep blue joy tinged with dawning awareness. Holding on carefully to her sanity, she trembled. 'On the first occasion you mention I was feeling hurt and angry, but I have no recollection of any second time. The only possible explanation must be that that night in the hut was the time when my memory began to return. I relived those dreadful hours all over again, and when you and the others broke in I must have cried out in delirium, not against you, but against the men terrifying my dreams. There can be no other explanation,' she assured him simply, 'not when, for hours previously

I'd been praying for you to arrive, had kept sane only by telling myself that somehow my need of you would be transmitted across the miles dividing us and you would know exactly where to find me. You came just as I knew you would, just as I hope you will always come whenever I feel need and longing for the man I love . . ..'

It was a wonderful sensation, being plucked like a piece of flotsam and gathered into the haven of his arms. Like the breaking of a dam too long under pressure, the force of his passion erupted and she was caught, submerged, drowned by waves of delight. She suffered ecstatic agony under a grip unconsciously cruel, then melting tenderness as the first powerful surge was controlled into a sweet stream of endearments, caresses, and hunger-filled kisses that reduced her to a quivering bundle of happiness held tightly against his pounding heart.

'Tell me, let me hear it again ... *say* it!' he groaned, his possessive lips swooping to capture a pulse hammering frantically in her slender neck.

'I love you, my thunderous Viking,' she whispered. 'I adore your gentle strength, your overpowering tenderness and your brutally possessive touch . . .'

His fiery head lifted so he could look his fill of her radiant face, flushed, confused, brimming over with love for *him*, the unhappy Halden, the dour, dominating Dane.

'How wrong my father was!' His brilliant green glance roved her trembling mouth, anticipating its sweetness. 'And how I pity Britt, poor misguided fool . . .'

When she dimpled his eyes blazed flame. 'I've just remembered! Janice suggested I might already be married, but I'm not——'

'But very soon will be!' he declared masterfully. 'The licence is burning a hole in my pocket!' He set a seal on his vow with a tender kiss, then teased, 'Every day I'll bring you an apple polished with love, or a posy of flowers—or best of all,' he glinted, 'I shall find some handy corner in which to give you a quick hug...' Their lips clung as they laughed, sharing their first secret joke, then humour was swamped as desire flared, urgent, demanding, searing as flame.

'How soon will you marry me, Raine?' he pleaded hoarsely. 'I've waited so long...'

A small chill feathered her happiness. 'As soon as you want, my darling.' Her dimple faded. 'You've made no secret of your need of a wife—any wife,' she breathed.

He sensed her mental withdrawal. Held close in his arms she had become distant, separated by the ghost of departed words. Yet their affinity was so complete he knew exactly the reassurance she needed.

'Not *any* wife, my dearest love, just one particular one. The one I plotted and schemed to win by appealing to her for assistance in mastering the art of courtship, *her courtship*,' he stressed, 'had I but dared own up to it. How else could I have got near enough to make you aware of me as a potential husband? Who but you would have taken the trouble to try to put a sparkle on rough jet?'

She stared. 'Black-hearted rogue!' she gasped,

then melted into laughter that was silenced by lips imprinting and demanding love.

'Promise you'll always love me!' begged the tall, imposing skipper of men.

And was reassured by a look from blue eyes so dependent they begged leave of him to live.

Have You Missed Any of These
Harlequin Romances?

Have You Missed Any of These
Harlequin Romances?

Have you missed any of these . . .

Harlequin Presents..

All books listed are available at **95c each** at your local bookseller or through the Harlequin Reader Service.

Have you missed any of these . . .

Harlequin Presents..

All books listed 95c

Harlequin Presents novels are available at your
or through the Harlequin Reader Service
Niagara Falls, N.Y. 14302; Canadian a
Stratford, Ontario N5A 6W4.